INTEGRATIVE NUTRITION

FAST TRACK WORKBOOK

YOUR GUIDE TO A SUCCESSFUL HEALTH COUNSELING CAREER

Published by Integrative Nutrition Publishing, Inc.
3 East 28 Street
New York, NY 10016
integrativenutrition.com

For ordering information or special discounts for bulk purchases, please contact
Integrative Nutrition Publishing, Inc.

Design and composition by Greenleaf Book Group LLC

The information in this book is not intended as a substitute for legal advice.
The publisher and author expressly disclaim responsibility for any and all unforeseen
consequences arising from use of the information contained herein. If you want the help
of a trained professional, consult an attorney licensed to practice in your state.

This book has been published to support the success of our students.
We are committed to educating our students to lead healthy, fulfilling lives with
a desired career and we are happy to provide the latest, most accurate information.

Publisher's Cataloging-In-Publication Data
(Prepared by The Donohue Group, Inc.)

Fast track workbook : your guide to a successful health counseling career.

p. : ill. ; cm.

ISBN: 978-0-9795264-1-1

1. Health counseling--Vocational guidance--Handbooks, manuals, etc. 2.
Nutrition counseling--Vocational guidance--Handbooks, manuals, etc. I. Title:
Integrative nutrition

R727.4 .F27 2008
362.1/04256/023   2008938330

Part of the Tree Neutral™ program that offsets the number of trees consumed
in printing this book by taking proactive steps such as planting trees in direct
proportion to the number of trees used. www.treeneutral.com

Printed in the United States of America on acid-free paper

08 09 10 11 12 13   10 9 8 7 6 5 4 3 2 1

Second Edition

ACKNOWLEDGMENTS

Joshua Rosenthal for his visionary leadership, commitment and unending support of Integrative Nutrition students, alumni and staff.

Robert Notter for his dedication to the school and brilliant evolution of the Fast Track Program and *Fast Track Workbook*.

Suzanne Boothby and Rachel Martin for their attention to detail and dedication to the school.

Integrative Nutrition Staff for being the most intelligent and committed group of people around.

Integrative Nutrition Students for inspiring us with their passion for learning and desire to help others.

Integrative Nutrition Alumni for blazing the trail to a new future of health and happiness in America and the world.

Current and Future Health Counseling Clients for their commitment to personal growth and their trust in the six-month program.

Our Mission is to play a crucial role in improving health and happiness in America, and through that process, create a ripple effect that transforms the world.

TABLE OF CONTENTS

Never doubt that a small group of thoughtful, committed citizens can change the world; indeed, it's the only thing that ever has.

—Margaret Mead,
famous anthropologist

INTRODUCTION

Clearly, our current healthcare system is not getting people healthy. Food-related disease is the number one cause of preventable death in the United States. Poor diet is linked to certain types of cancer, obesity, diabetes and heart disease. Other health conditions, such as headaches, ADD, IBS, asthma and allergies are rapidly increasing in the U.S. and spreading around the world as other countries adopt our way of life and our eating habits. As a result, more people are on prescriptions, medication costs are soaring, health insurance prices are higher than ever before and doctors spend less time with their patients. Increasing medications and operations is not the answer to our current health dilemma. Prevention through diet and lifestyle is the answer. People are still gaining weight and getting sick despite abundant advice to eat more fruits and vegetables, exercise, and cut out junk food. We desperately need straightforward, honest advice on how to become healthier.

As a student at The Institute for Integrative Nutrition, you will gain fundamental and practical knowledge of nutrition and how to live a balanced life. This information will help you find a new level of health and happiness in your life and positively influence other people. Step out and use this education to influence a world that desperately needs your help. You may fear this work and want to procrastinate getting started. We encourage you to take action and move beyond being only a consumer of information. Get out there and educate people on your beliefs.

If you are passionate about health and want a life and career that you love, this is a great career for you. We are here to teach you and guide you through the process. Our curriculum will show you how to develop a successful business as a Health Counselor, step-by-step. As a student at Integrative Nutrition, you will learn how to share your education with friends, family, and the general public and those people who you touch will influence the people whom they encounter. As Health Counselors we have the ability to create a ripple effect that will improve the lives of people around the world.

Our mission is to play a crucial role in improving the health and happiness in America, and through that process, create a ripple effect that transforms the world. With your dedication and hard work, we can make this happen. Thank you for choosing our school and thank you for following your heart. Let's get started!

This is your life,
not a dress rehearsal!

—Joshua Rosenthal

HOW TO USE THIS BOOK

FOLLOW OUR SIMPLE INSTRUCTIONS

Building a business does not have to be complicated. This book, along with the curriculum taught in class, outlines our simple, time-tested process for starting your practice. Along the way you may find yourself distracted by details or tempted to overcomplicate things. Relax and stay focused. Follow our simple instructions, and you will experience success.

MAKE IT YOUR OWN

Just as there is no one diet that is right for everyone, there is no one business plan that is best for every counselor. The information in this book reflects our years of experience helping counselors build successful businesses. Not every suggestion will be right for you, so use your intuition and intelligence to personalize these business strategies.

GET SUPPORT

Starting your own business will be a new, challenging experience for many of you. Our community provides tremendous support to make this happen. Ask your counselor, the Online Education Forum (OEF), your buddy and your fellow students for any help that you need. Hold local study chapters related to business topics. Enlist your friends and family to cheer you on or to provide expert advice from their fields. Having a support team increases your chances of success.

DO THE EXERCISES

Even though they may seem simple, the exercises in this book are carefully designed to walk you through the process of starting your business. We have created sections for notes throughout this workbook, so make a mess of it.

USE YOUR WHOLE EDUCATION

Don't just rely only on this book to teach you how to start a business as a Health Counselor. The class weekends, conferences and focus classes all provide critical information about how to be successful. This book is just one part of your curriculum. It supplements what you learn in class.

GO AT YOUR OWN PACE (BUT DON'T PROCRASTINATE)

This book contains a lot of information, and you don't have to do everything all at once. Some of these steps will be easy and fun for you. Others will be more challenging. Build your business at your own pace.

INTEGRATIVE NUTRITION

FAST TRACK WORKBOOK

YOUR GUIDE TO A SUCCESSFUL HEALTH COUNSELING CAREER

If one advances confidently in the direction of his dreams, and endeavors to live the life which he has imagined, he will meet with success unexpected in common hours.

—Henry David Thoreau

CHAPTER 1:

STARTING ON YOUR ROAD TO SUCCESS

Congratulations! You are on your way to becoming a certified Health Counselor. The key to having success in this endeavor is to maintain a deep level of focus. Treat this year at Integrative Nutrition as if you were in Harvard Medical School. Work hard, pay attention, make your education a priority and follow the guidelines we set forth, and you will experience success.

Health counseling is a process in which a Health Counselor guides a client to reach his or her health and life goals by making step-by-step changes to his or her diet and lifestyle. The process typically involves a six-month program. The client learns about new, healthy foods and the concept of primary foods: relationships, physical activity, career and spirituality. The Health Counselor works with the client to set goals to gradually incorporate improved primary and secondary foods into the client's life. Health counseling is completely focused on the client—where the client is and where he or she wants to go with his or her health and life. The Health Counselor acts as a guide, helping the client to gain control of and responsibility for his or her health.

CAREER ASSESSMENT

At this time, we ask that you reflect on your reasons for wanting to become a certified Health Counselor. Maybe it is to help other people, or maybe you want to learn how to best feed yourself. Perhaps you want to leave your current job and create a new career that you are passionate about. Whatever your reasons, please consider the following questions:

Notes:

What are you doing in your current career?

Selling gym memberships
Setting people on the right fitness track
Educating about personal training

On a scale of 1 – 10, how much do you enjoy your career?

Uninspired   Satisfied   Extremely Satisfied

1   2   3   4   5   **(6)**   7   8   9   10

What are five things you like about your current career?

1. Friendships I've made
2. Lives I've changed - Matthew
3. Knowledge re: PT
4. Location
5. Ability to help/brighten people's days

What are five things you wish you could change about your current career?

1. Salary
2. Pressure re: sales
3. Close-out hours
4. Pipeline pressure
5. Being Inside

Please list your top five reasons for wanting to become a Health Counselor:

1. Help people
2. Help myself
3. Spread knowledge
4. Be my own boss
5. Be in control of my $$$

CAREER OPPORTUNITIES

So many opportunities are available for working in the health counseling field. Your personal and professional interests can help shape the design of your business. You can choose the path you most enjoy. Doing this work gives you the ability to help many people in ways you may not have previously imagined. You will be able to work with clients one-on-one and in groups. If you want to address large groups, you will receive training to give lectures and other public speaking engagements. You can work in corporate wellness and help organizations change the health of their employees. You could choose to work in a spa, a yoga studio or in a doctor's office. You also have the opportunity to become involved in advocacy and outreach work. Additionally, you may find yourself inspired to write a book, create information products, design customized health programs, or even be on television or on the radio. Whatever path you choose, you have the opportunity to do work you love and be an instrument of change in your community and for the world.

CONFIDENCE, CONFIDENCE, CONFIDENCE!

The main thing that prevents our students from starting businesses as Health Counselors is thinking they don't know enough. It causes you to get stuck in what we call "paralyzation and procrastination." You put everything ahead of health counseling, saying that your life is too busy or you have more important things to do, but underlying all of this is the belief that you may not be good enough. We do not want this to happen to you. Chances are you are an incredibly intelligent and gifted person who has a knack for helping others. It is important for you to recognize that not everyone has these gifts.

To become a successful Health Counselor, you must work to increase your level of self-esteem and confidence. You are an incredibly unique person with a lot to offer the world. It is essential that you become familiar with your strengths, and that you are able to communicate them to other people. Please take a moment now to evaluate what you believe are your greatest qualities.

Notes:

List the top eight here:

1. Likeable
2. Friendly
3. True desire to help others
4. Motivating
5. High energy that's contagious
6. Passionate about health
7. Angry w/ processed food + gov't
8. Want to help make changes

YOUR VISION

You are ultimately in charge of your business and the direction you'd like to go. The clearer your intentions and vision for your practice become, the more likely it is that you will be successful. Your vision, or mission, is simply what you would like to accomplish in your business. It is the compass for your business and gives you direction on how to move forward with purpose and clarity. This vision will keep you going every day, even when things are not going so well or according to your plan.

It is important to consider why you do this work and your higher goals for your business. Explore the difference you want to make with this work and what influence you want to have on your clients. This will help give you a roadmap from which you can move forward. Focus on your vision every day. Let it inspire and guide you to reach your goals and be successful. You may even want to write your vision out on a piece of paper and put it on your wall or someplace where you will see it frequently.

Why do you want to do this work?

What motivates you?

....

....

....

....

....

....

What type of person do you want to help?

....

....

....

....

....

....

What difference do you want to make in the world?

....

....

....

....

....

....

When are you inspired?

....

....

....

....

....

....

Notes:

Notes:

What is your life's purpose?

....

....

....

....

....

....

YOUR GOALS

Now we would like you to think about what you want to do with your education at the school. What are your goals for building your health counseling business? How do they fit in with goals you have for other aspects of your life? This process will help clarify what you want to accomplish. In each section, please be sure to list at least one goal related to health counseling, such as the number of health histories you want to do, the number of clients you want to have, when you want to leave your current job, what kind of clients you'd like to work with or how much money you'd like to make. During the coming months, you will be taking consistent action to make these goals a reality.

What are three goals you have for the next week?

1. IPOD
2. ITOUCH
3. Go on OEF more

What are three goals you have for the next month?

1. Up-to-date on modules
2. Mtg 6.21
3. Move forward w/ shopper idea

What are three goals you have for the next six months?

1. Finish my studies
2. Progress w/ shopper idea
3. Have 3 clients

What are three goals you have for the next year?

1. Health counseling PT
2. Working w/ corporate comp.
3. Shoppe idea taking off

What are three goals you have for the next two years?

1. Full on nutritionist lifestyle
2. Perhaps studying more
3. Engaged

What are two goals you have for the next 10 years?

1. Wife
2. Mother
   Happy :)

Notes:

TAKING CARE OF YOU

Starting a new career as a Health Counselor is exciting and rewarding. For most of you, it's an opportunity to do what you love, while simultaneously helping others. However, starting a new business can be challenging at first. For this reason, we want you to take incredibly good care of yourself this year. In order to be a successful Health Counselor, you have to be healthy, happy, well rested and in balance. To support you in taking care of yourself while building your business, we will continuously do exercises, both in class and in this book, to help you stay in balance. In addition, you will have the support of your individual Health Counselor throughout the program to help you stay on track with self-care. We want you to be healthy and happy throughout the process and graduate from the school feeling better than ever.

PRIMARY FOOD

At Integrative Nutrition, we have coined the phrase "primary food." Primary food feeds us but doesn't come on a plate. When our primary foods are balanced and fulfilling, our lives feed us, making what we eat secondary.

We group primary foods into four categories: healthy relationships, regular physical activity, a desired career and a spiritual practice. We invite you to look at these areas of your life from a new perspective—as a form of nutrition. This is especially important when starting this new career because being at your best will make other people want to work with you.

Notes:

Consider these four areas of your life: relationships, physical activity, career and spirituality. Write a short paragraph about each, describing any imbalances you may have in these areas and any actions you'd like to take to create more balance.

How are your relationships?

....

....

....

....

....

....

How is your physical activity?

....

....

....

....

....

....

How is your career?

....

....

....

....

....

....

How is your spiritual practice?

....

....

Notes:

POSITIVE THINKING

Henry Ford once said, "Whether you think that you can or that you can't, you are usually right." When it comes to health counseling, this is definitely true. Believing in yourself is key to success.

Start to envision yourself as a Health Counselor. What does your life look like as a successful Health Counselor? What do your days look like? Are you full-time or part-time? What kind of clients do you work with? Where do you see your clients? When do you work? What other types of services might you offer? What do you do in your free time? Who are the key support people in your life? What health concerns have you cleared up? What else is going on in your life?

Unfortunately, we seldom have an abundance of positive thoughts in our heads. Most of us have a tendency to focus on the things in our life that are not working. At Integrative Nutrition we always ask, "What is new and good?" This question breaks the habit of focusing on negative thoughts. By focusing on positive thoughts, you will attract more good into your life because what you put your attention on will grow.

What are three things that are going well in your life now?

1. Apt!!
2. Summer!
3. Commute to work!

What are three things that are going well for you so far at Integrative Nutrition?

1. Passed tests
2. got biz cards
3. healthy diet

What are three things you are looking forward to about health counseling?

1. Changing lives
2. Helping others
3. Spreading knowledge

Start to pay attention to where your mind goes most of the time. How much of your attention is on what is not going well in your life? How much attention is on what is going well?

You can incorporate positive thinking into your life in many different ways. Some simple ways are to ask people what is new and good, brag to others about what is going well with you (and then let them brag back), consciously put your mind on positive thoughts or write everything you are grateful for in a journal. Practice different ways to increase positive thinking in your life and see what works best for you. The Integrative Nutrition Journal is a great tool that incorporates food and lifestyle with gratitude and goal setting. Also, use your Health Counselor and your buddy for support by sharing with them what is going well in your life. Notice how you create your own reality. When you practice positive thinking, your world begins to look brighter.

GETTING OUT OF YOUR OWN WAY

As you reflect on the exercise above, you'll notice what a difference it can make when you focus on the positive things in your life and the goals you want to accomplish. Often, it is very easy for us to think about how we are "not good enough," and we wonder if we have what it takes to be successful in business. Our inner critic likes to tell us that we have faults or that other people know more than we do. It's important to recognize this inner voice and take steps to lessen its potential effect on you. If you listen to your doubts, or if you let your fears get in the way, you may not take the steps needed to attain the success you truly desire. If you are able to catch the negative thought patterns and then recognize that they truly have no power over you, you can move forward more easily.

When you really stop to think about it, you will understand that you have a lot to offer your friends, family, clients and yourself, by being a Health Counselor. Use these steps to help you minimize any potential self-limiting beliefs before they sabotage your efforts:

- When a fear or negative thought comes up, stop and recognize that the thought is there. Take a deep breath, and notice how you feel.
- Check in with yourself, and notice that the thought only has power over you if you allow it to.
- Ask yourself, "Do I know for sure that this thought is true?" or "What is the worst that can happen if I take this action or do this marketing step?"
- Focus on turning your negative thought around and choose a different thought that causes you less anxiety or fear.
- Figure out how to keep your mind focused on your goals and believe in yourself.
- Take step-by-step actions towards your goals, and don't let your fears hold you back.
- Keep practicing, continue this process and trust yourself.

CREATING A BUSINESS MIND

As you start your education and learn the skills needed to build your practice, it's important to cultivate your mindset. Believe it or not, once you begin this work you are a business owner, whether you end up doing health counseling full-time or part-time. As such, you'll need to start thinking like a business person. Consider what it will take for you to be successful, how you will talk about your work, the confidence you will project, the structure of your time, and in general the ways you can present a professional image to the world. Start practicing what it is like to be more professional and concise in your emails and in conversations, especially when you talk about your training at the school. Ask yourself, "How would a successful business person behave in this situation?" Focus on building your confidence, and trust that you know enough to try the marketing tips you'll learn in this book and in class. And most importantly, take action every week towards building your business.

PERSONAL MANAGEMENT

To be successful in doing this work and building your business, it's important to develop an initial structure so that you consistently have time to read the *Fast Track Workbook: Your Guide to a Successful Health Counseling Career.* Do the exercises, follow the recommendations in class, and start putting yourself out there to set up, organize and develop your practice. If you have consistent time in your schedule each week to learn, practice, and reach out for support, you will be more likely to succeed. Take a moment now and think about when you will find time for your business.

Which day(s) of the week do you have time to devote towards your business?

....

....

....

....

....

What time on that day(s) will you spend on these activities?

....

....

....

....

Notes:

ORGANIZATION

Now that you are learning to become a Health Counselor, it's time to start thinking of yourself as a business owner. Although this may seem overwhelming, if you take it one step at a time, you will be just fine.

Use the following section to see if you have your basic necessities covered. If you answer "no" to any of these questions, you will want to take action to change your answer to "yes" as soon as possible.

BASIC OFFICE SUPPLIES

1. Do you have a phone? **(Yes/No)**

   If you have more than one phone number, have you chosen which one you will use for your business? **(Yes/No)**

   What is the number for your business? ....

   Have you changed your voicemail or answering machine greeting so that it is professional? (e.g., "This is Jane Smith, Health Counselor. I cannot take your call right now, so please leave a message and I'll get back to you as soon as possible. Have a great day!") **(Yes/No)**

2. Do you have a professional email address? (e.g., jsmith@yahoo.com) **(Yes/No)**

   If you have more than one email address, have you chosen which one you will use for your business? **(Yes/No)**

   What is your email address? ....

   If you do not have one, or you have one that is not professional, choose one here:

   ....

Note: You can get free email at yahoo.com, hotmail.com or gmail.com. We suggest that you use your name if possible (e.g., janedoe@yahoo.com) rather than something less professional, such as jane623@yaho.com).

3. Do you have the following office supplies?

   File Folders: **(Yes/No)**

   Pens: **(Yes/No)**

   Pads of Paper: **(Yes/No)**

   File Holder: **(Yes/No)**

   Computer or Pocket Calendar/Scheduling System: **(Yes/No)**

   Paper Clips/Staples: **(Yes/No)**

4. Do you have a printer or access to a local copy shop, Kinkos or a library? **(Yes/No)**

ORGANIZATIONAL SYSTEMS

As a Health Counselor, you will have appointments, follow-ups, lectures, cooking classes and events. You do not want to lose any information. There are various types of organizational systems.

FILE FOLDERS

Paper-filing systems can be very helpful. If you do not have filing cabinets, you can buy small, portable filing cabinets or boxes that fit file folders. You can get these supplies at Staples, Hold Everything or the Container Store. Once you have your filing cabinet, you will need hanging files and file folders. To keep things neat and organized, place only one folder in each hanging file.

Here are some suggested labels for your hanging files:

- **Health History Forms:** We'll discuss what the Health History Form is in Chapter 2: "Health History Consultations."

- **Completed Health History Forms:** People who did not become clients have filled these out. People who become paying clients will get their own folder, and their Health History Form will go into that folder.

- **Health History Notes:** Store your ideas about what worked and what you want to improve.

- **Handouts:** Hard copies of all of your health counseling handouts.

- **Clients:** Within this file, each client should have his or her own hanging file to keep that client's documents.

- **Financial Information:** Store copies of payment checks, receipts and any other pertinent financial information.

- **Articles:** Keep articles you collect and want to share with clients.

COMPUTER ORGANIZATION

Along with your file folders and paper-work, you will also want to create computer folders to save important information relevant to your business. We will provide you with many resources including forms, handouts, outlines and other documents to get your business started. Once you get these, we recommend you save them onto the hard drive of your computer. We suggest that you also create the following folders on your computer's desktop to help you stay organized with your health counseling information and documents.

- **Health Counseling:** Within this folder you will create another folder for Health History Forms and a folder for client handouts.
- **Classes:** Within this folder, you can create a new folder for each talk you give (e.g., Sugar Blues, Eating for Energy).
- **Newsletters:** Store drafts of your newsletters.
- **Marketing:** Keep track of business marketing ideas.

COMPUTER FILES OR FILE FOLDERS

Even if you are extremely computer savvy, please know that you cannot keep everything on your computer when it comes to health counseling. Your clients will be filling out Health History Forms in person, and you will have other documents that you will want to save. You should have an actual file folder for each client that contains his or her paperwork, as detailed above.

SCHEDULE ORGANIZATION

Some people prefer to do all their scheduling electronically, either on their computer, Blackberry or smart phone, or a Palm Pilot. Other people prefer to use an old-fashioned pocket, desk or wall calendar. Use what works best for you. Being organized means putting everything into your schedule. You should schedule when you plan to exercise, when you are having dinner with your family and every other little detail. Even if it is something that you are sure you won't forget, if you don't put it in your schedule, your chances of forgetting about it or double-booking yourself are much higher. Your scheduling system should be foolproof. The benefit to having a pocket calendar or handheld device is that you can always have it on you. Electronic scheduling systems like Microsoft Outlook will also set off reminders, which is great if you are a forgetful person or like to have that extra reminder.

CONTACT ORGANIZATION

As you begin your health counseling business, you will meet many, people. Some of these people will be potential clients, others will be contacts who may be able to refer

EMBRACE TECHNOLOGY

Some people are afraid of technology. Are you avoiding technology? Do you know how to use your computer, email, phone and other devices? As a Health Counselor, your time is invaluable and using technology can certainly save you time. By learning how to work with technology, you can benefit from the fast level of service that it provides. Also, 90 percent of your clients will have good technological skills and will expect you to communicate with them in this way. This is part of providing good customer service.

Here are a few fundamental things you should know how to do on your computer:

- Print
- Read email
- Send email
- Cut and paste
- Save email into folders
- Send attachments over email
- Create Microsoft Word documents
- Use CDs and discs with your computer

If you do not know how to do something from the list above, identify someone in your life who could show you. Perhaps you have a friend or family member who is good with computers.

clients to you or help your business in some other way. You will want to keep track of important people you meet so that you can be sure to follow up with them when needed. Some people like to keep track of all their contacts on their computer, while others prefer a hard copy notepad or Rolodex. Any way that works for you is great. Just make sure that you are doing something to stay organized. It will also allow you to track the conversations and interactions you have with potential clients, business partners, or other organizations with whom you may do business. This will help with your marketing efforts and all of the tasks required to keep building these relationships.

If you choose to keep track of your potential clients on your computer, you have a couple of options. One is to keep track of your contacts by using a contact management software package such as Act! (www.act.com), or Maximer Entrepreneur Edition (www.maximizer.com). These programs allow you to store contact and client information and track any communications you have with those people. You can also create an Excel spreadsheet for your contacts.

If you do not wish to purchase a contact management software package or create an Excel spreadsheet, you can do the same kind of tracking in a low-tech kind of way.

Some people prefer to keep track of their acquaintances using a Rolodex or simple address book, or you can use the following form to record information about people you meet. You can store these forms either in a hanging file or an online folder you create for "Contacts."

TAKE ACTION

Throughout the coming months, you are going to learn a great deal of information about health and nutrition by coming to class, listening to the Guest Speakers, reading the books, participating in the OEF and speaking with your individual Health Counselor. However, it is in seeing clients while you are a student in the Professional Training Program (PTP) that you will get the most out of this education.

The current trend in America is consumerism. People are used to buying a product and then owning it. We encourage you to break this trend when it comes to your education at Integrative Nutrition. Instead of merely absorbing the information we teach and keeping it inside your brain, we want you to go out and teach others what you are learning here. Make your education an active experience.

It is through your work with clients that our curriculum will genuinely start to make sense to you. You will see how desperately in need most people are of someone to talk to about their health. By taking on clients, you will learn to become a leader and a partner in the change that is happening around health in this country. As you teach others to eat more nutritious foods and balance their lives, you will notice that you too experience growth, improved health, increased happiness and more fulfillment.

We will tell you when you are ready to start seeing clients in a six-month program. Some of you will get one client; some of you will get 20. It is required that you have at least two clients before graduation. Your clients will pay you, or maybe you will barter services. Either way, it is extremely important that you start seeing clients while you are in the school because you will then have the weekend classes, your Health Counselor and the community of students to support you and answer any questions that may come up.

You can practice the health history consultation, a free initial consultation with a prospective client, while you are waiting to work with actual clients. The next chapter will explain everything you need to know about health histories.

Throughout the years, we have seen many students who come to class, learn all about nutrition, improve their own health and plan to do health counseling after they graduate. But this plan rarely works. These people end up putting off getting clients and never get around to it. You do not want to be one of these people. We encourage you to use the school to help you improve your own health and then go out to help others.

CLIENT CONTACT FORM

CLIENT CONTACT INFORMATION

Name: (the person's name and what they prefer to be called)

Client Source: (e.g., friend, referral, networking event, co-worker)

Cell Phone: (their main contact #s)

Work Phone:

Email: (their permanent email address)

Address:

City, State, Zip:

Special Information: (put any special details here about the client: perhaps the work they do, the name of their dog, their spouse or partner, anything that is important and that by your remembering, makes them feel special.)

CLIENT CORRESPONDENCES

(Date)	(write down what you talked about, what you need to follow up with and when.)
(2/21/08)	(Initial call to set up health history. Scheduled for 3/22/08 at 7 pm in the lobby of the Marriott. Email her on 3/21 with reminder notice.)
(other dates here)	

GRADUATE PROFILE

NAOKO IKEDA
Harrison, NY
naoko@nourished-living.com
2006 Graduate

I had trouble sleeping the night before because I was so nervous. I kept it small and invited only people I knew. The first few minutes were uncomfortable, but by the middle of the talk I felt connected to the group and saw that they were really enjoying themselves and getting something out of it. As I continued to do more public speaking, I learned to relax more, be myself and have fun. Now my talks and workshops are so powerful because they create community and connection among my clients and prospective clients.

> "...when you take care of yourself and organize your life, you get the right clients at the right time."

I've found it's really important to present myself in a professional way. Before I step outside each day, I believe I am a Health Counselor and move with that intention. I remind myself why I am doing this. I feel I am in demand. I'm not being pushy or asking anyone for a favor. What's amazing is that when you take care of yourself and organize your life, you get the right clients at the right time. So many people need us, so get out there and be confident!

The school provides all the outlines and materials you need, so don't reinvent the wheel. You can make it more your own whenever you are ready. At first, keep it simple and work with what you have. I got my business rolling because I didn't wait until I was perfectly ready. My price increased as my confidence and skills improved.

I love being a motivator for clients to get excited about themselves. I give them the energy to tap into their talents and live authentically. I help them find their strengths and let them shine through. I particularly enjoy helping stressed-out women prioritize their health goals. I teach them to nurture themselves, which in turn improves every aspect of their lives. As I help increase the quality of my clients' lives, I am improving the quality of my own life. I can't ask for a more fulfilling career!

I was a business analyst when I came to Integrative Nutrition, but halfway through the school year I left my job to pursue health counseling full-time and teach fitness classes part-time. I love being my own boss. I have a home office, so I no longer have to commute. I'm making measurable differences in peoples' lives rather than feeling that I don't matter as an employee. I'm amazed at how quickly everything changed!

From the day I signed up for the program, I consistently told friends, family, colleagues and acquaintances that I was becoming a Health Counselor. I got a buzz going before starting to see clients in January. I was proactive and took it one step at a time, following the instructions the school gave us. I felt inspired and empowered, and I used the support from the school to take charge of my life. When I graduated in June, I had 17 paying clients!

Public speaking has always been one of my biggest fears, but with the school's help, I actually learned to love it. The first time I led a workshop,

Notes:

Begin somewhere;
you cannot build a reputation
on what you intend to do.

—Liz Smith,
author and journalist

CHAPTER 2:

HEALTH HISTORY CONSULTATIONS

The way to get more clients is to schedule health history consultations. A health history is a free initial consultation that gives both you and your potential client a chance to get to know one another and determine whether or not you want to work together. The potential client gets to see what you're about—how you work and what you offer. And you get to decide whether or not the other person is someone you want to work with. Because the session is free, you are going to be more likely to have people willing to meet with you than if they had to pay for it.

THE HEALTH HISTORY FORM

Here are the Health History Forms. You want to become very familiar with these documents. Take a moment now to look at all the questions. On the first page are questions about the person's lifestyle and health—where they were born, what they do for a living, what their main health concern is, etc. On the back is a section about food, where the person can tell you what they ate as a child, what they ate a year ago and what they are eating now. There are specific forms for men and women, please review both.

WOMEN'S CONFIDENTIAL HEALTH HISTORY
PLEASE WRITE OR PRINT CLEARLY

Name:..

Address:..

Email address:... How often do you check email?..................................

Telephone—Work: .... Home: .... Cell: ....

Age:........................ Height: .... Date of Birth: .... Place of Birth: ....

Current weight: .... Weight six months ago: .... One year ago: ....

Would you like your weight to be different? .... If so, what?.............................

Relationship status: ....

Children: .... Pets: ....

Occupation: .... Hours of work per week:...................

Please list your main health concerns: ....
....
....

At what point in your life did you feel your best? ....

Other concerns or goals? ....
....

Any serious illness/hospitalizations/injuries? ....
....

How is the health of your mother?..

How is the health of your father?...

What is your ancestry?.. What blood type are you? ....

Do you sleep well? .... How many hours?.................... Do you wake up at night?...............

Why?..

Any pain, stiffness or swelling? ....

Are your periods regular?........................... How many days is your flow?.................. How frequent?..............

Painful or symptomatic?.................... Please explain: ....
....

Birth control history:...
....

Do you experience yeast infections or urinary tract infections? .... Please explain: ....

....

Constipation/Diarrhea/Gas? Please explain: ....

Allergies or sensitivities? Please explain: ....

Do you take any supplements or medications? Please list: ....

....

Any healers, helpers, or therapies with which you are involved? Please list: ....

....

What role do sports and exercise play in your life? ....

....

What foods did you eat often as a child?

Breakfast	Lunch	Dinner	Snacks	Liquids

What's your food like these days?

Breakfast	Lunch	Dinner	Snacks	Liquids

Will family and friends be supportive of your desire to make food and/or lifestyle changes? ....

What percentage of your food is home cooked? .... Do you cook? ....

Where do you get the rest from? ....

Do you crave sugar, coffee, cigarettes, or have any major addictions? ....

....

The most important thing I should change about my diet to improve my health is: ....

....

....

MEN'S CONFIDENTIAL HEALTH HISTORY
PLEASE WRITE OR PRINT CLEARLY

Name:..

Address:..

Email address:... How often do you check email?..

Telephone—Work: .... Home: .... Cell:.............................

Age:............................ Height: .... Date of Birth: .... Place of Birth:.....................

Current weight:.............................. Weight six months ago:.............................. One year ago:........................

Would you like your weight to be different?.......... If so, what? ....

Relationship status: ....

Children: .... Pets: ....

Occupation:.. Hours of work per week: ....

Please list your main health concerns: ....

....

....

At what point in your life did you feel your best? ....

Other concerns and/or goals? ....

....

Any serious illnesses/hospitalizations/injuries? ....

....

How is the health of your mother?..

How is the health of your father?...

What is your ancestry? .... What blood type are you? ....

Do you sleep well? .... How many hours?........................... Do you wake up at night?.................

Why?..

Any pain, stiffness or swelling? ....

Constipation/Diarrhea/Gas?.......................... Plese explain:..

Allergies or sensitivities? Please explain: ....

....

Do you take any supplements or medications? Please list: ....

Any healers, helpers, pets or therapies with which you are involved? Please list:..

....

What role do sports and exercise play in your life?...

....

What foods did you eat often as a child?

Breakfast	Lunch	Dinner	Snacks	Liquids

What's your food like these days?

Breakfast	Lunch	Dinner	Snacks	Liquids

Will family and/or friends be supportive of your desire to make food and/or lifestyle changes? ....

What percentage of your food is home cooked?... Do you cook?.........................

Where do you get the rest from?...

Do you crave sugar, coffee, cigarettes, or have any major addictions? ....

....

The most important thing I should change about my diet to improve my health is: ....

....

Anything else you'd like to share? ....

....

THE HEALTH HISTORY CONSULTATION

We'll discuss later in this chapter how to find and invite people to come to your free initial health history consultation. But first, let's review what will happen before, during and after the consultation.

BEFORE THE HEALTH HISTORY CONSULTATION

- Decide where you are going to hold the consultation: at home, an office, on the phone, in a hotel lobby, or in a tea or coffee shop

- Send a reminder email a day or two before your appointment. In this email, give directions for where to meet you, and let the person know you look forward to seeing them. If the person does not regularly use email, you can call instead. Or, if you are doing the session by phone, remind them of the date and time and the number to call you on (unless you prefer calling them.)

- Pick an outfit that is professional, yet comfortable.

- Make sure you have a blank Health History Form, a pen and a clipboard to write on.

- Center yourself by quieting your mind right before the meeting.

BEGINNING THE HEALTH HISTORY CONSULTATION

- When you greet the person, give them a warm welcome. Show them you are happy to see them. Acknowledge the potential client's presence, and thank them for taking the time to talk with you.

- Connect by touch—shaking hands or hugging if appropriate. If you are on the phone, make sure they know you are happy to be talking with them.

- Give the person the Health History Form to fill out on a clipboard or something that makes it easy to write on. It is best to have them fill out the form at the beginning of the session while they are with you. Filling out the form can be an emotional process, so it is good that you are there to provide support and address whatever comes up. If you prefer, you can have them fill out the form ahead of time and bring it with them to your session. This may be a better option if you know you have a limited amount of time. You can also email the form ahead of time and have the person fill it out and email it back to you. But again, we recommend doing it together in case anything emotional comes up.

- Offer the person some water or tea, and get it while they are filling out the form.

- If the session is on the phone, have a blank form in front of you before the call begins. Then you can ask the questions and fill in the answers as you go through the form.

- Once you have the completed form in front of you, you can begin the conversation. Here are some sample questions you might ask to get the conversation started:

> "So, how was filling out this form for you?"
> "What's new and good in your life?"
> "How do you feel about coming to a health history consultation?"

DURING THE HEALTH HISTORY CONSULTATION

- Use the form to guide you. Go through the form in order. Ask questions based on what the person wrote on the sheet. Let them talk about everything, especially their main health concern. The form is meant to stimulate conversation. You may find that your potential client wants to talk more about one part of the form and less about another. That's okay. Go where the client wants to go.

- Go over easy information first. Where they live, where they are from, how old they are, etc. You can ask questions such as: "How does it feel being 36?", "How was it growing up in Nebraska?", "Do you like living in New York City?"

- Listen, connect and take notes. The more you listen, the more the person will open up. Connecting with the person will create trust. And if you take notes, the person will feel important. Avoid taking too many notes because you don't want to have your head in your paper the whole time.

- Breathe. Notice how much you like talking to and listening to this person. Empty your mind of everything that you have to do or any place you need to go. Stay present and trust yourself.

- When you get to the more complex subjects, such as weight, relationships, career and sleep, read between the lines and ask questions that draw the person out. For example, if the person wrote that they want their weight to be different, you can ask, "Do you want to look slimmer, feel lighter or both?" A good question to ask if you see they spend many hours working is, "I see that you work about 45 hours each week. Does that feel like a lot to you, or does it feel like you have a good balance of work, rest and play?" If they wrote that they don't sleep well and wake up a lot during the night, you can ask, "Why do you think that is?"

- People are not used to talking about their digestion in regular conversation, so you may find resistance around getting people to open up about constipation or diarrhea. It may be helpful to say something like, "Most people suffer from some kind of digestive problem. I see it all the time, and talking about digestion is one of the key elements to figuring out what foods are best for you." Or share something about yourself such as, "I used to have terrible constipation, but since I changed my diet, it's cleared up, which I'm thrilled about."

Notes:

Notes:

- If possible, make the person laugh. If you can get someone to laugh in your office, that is a huge step forward. Most people take healthcare too seriously. Having fun with the person will make them feel comfortable and lighten the mood.

- Do not give advice during the health history. We cannot stress this point enough. Let the person do the majority of the talking. Ask questions to take them deeper into what they are talking about. In the health history, you are simply gathering information and talking about your program. Once someone becomes your client, then you can start giving advice.

- Share how you relate to the person's issues. When someone knows that you are human too, and you have worked through your own health issues, they will feel closer to you. However, be careful to not talk about yourself too much. Mention some health conditions or health concerns that you have cleared up either once or twice throughout the health history.

- Remember and write down key points to bring up later in the conversation. If the person shared earlier that they take allergy medication, you can say, "When I am ready to start seeing clients, I can work with you to help you understand what is going on with your allergies."

- Notice if there are any areas of the form left blank. It could be that the person did not list something because they are avoiding it. Use your judgment. You may want to say, "I notice that you did not write anything down for this question. Why is that?"

- Restate and paraphrase what the person shares with you. This shows you understand what is being communicated to you and gives the person the opportunity to clarify anything that is unclear. When the person says something, you can say, "So what you are saying is…" or "What I'm hearing you say is…"

- Briefly explain the concept of primary and secondary foods. It will be helpful for the person if you talk about the importance of both what we eat and our lifestyle, how if we are not happy or fulfilled in one aspect of our life, such as relationship or career, we will not be healthy no matter what we eat. Remember to avoid giving them any advice. Simply introduce the concept.

- Do not avoid silence. Let the person speak and when they are done speaking, you don't have to start speaking right away. Sometimes if you allow silence, the person will take this as permission to go even further with their thoughts. Real healing can occur here. Even if the silence feels awkward to you, it's okay to experiment with allowing it.

- At the end of the health history, after you've gone over what the person is eating, ask, "What are three things you know you could be doing for your health that you are not currently doing?" Then write those things down. You will use them in your closing.

ENDING THE HEALTH HISTORY CONSULTATION

- Tell the person that you've really enjoyed getting to know them better and mention one specific thing that you liked about the session.

- Ask them, "How was that for you?" and "What was something you found valuable in our session?"

- Restate some of the health concerns the person mentioned and the three things they know they could be doing for their health. For example, you can say, "I know that your main concerns at this time are losing weight and having increased energy. It's great that you know eating less and working out more will help you with these goals. However, I find that most people know what they should be doing for their health, but they have difficulty actually doing it. If we were working together, I would be here to support you to reach your goals and make positive changes."

- If you are at the point in the program and are not yet seeing clients, you can end the health history here. You can simply tell the person that you are still in the training program and not seeing clients at this time. Once you are ready to work with them in your six-month program, you will contact them again to see how you can support them as a client to reach the goals you discussed during your consultation.

- Ask them, "Would you be interested in working with me when I am ready to see clients?" If they say yes, you can say something like, "Great! I'll follow up with you once I start seeing clients. What is the best way to get in touch with you?" It is important to take control of the process. You must contact them and follow up once you are ready to start seeing clients. Please make notes of all the people you need to follow up with, and have a comprehensive list that includes their contact information.

- Bonus Step: Ask them, "Do you know anyone else who you think may be interested in doing a health history with me?" If they do, get that person's contact information.

- We'll talk more in Chapter 5 "Successfully Signing on Clients" about how to end the health history consultation once you are ready to see clients!

AFTER THE HEALTH HISTORY CONSULTATION

- Follow up with the potential client via email or phone. Appreciate them, and mention something personal to make them feel special. Let them know you will keep them updated on when you are ready to start seeing clients.

- Keep a log of all your health histories in one place. You may want to create an Excel spreadsheet or use a piece of paper from your Health History folder. A suggested template is at the end of this chapter.

- Reflect on your session. What worked? What didn't work? Take notes for yourself and keep them in the binder, folder or notebook where you keep all your Health History information. Take a moment to realize that you are an amazing work in progress. Your counseling skills will only improve with time.

LISTENING

As mentioned earlier, you should do very little talking during the health history. People love to talk about themselves, especially with someone who is a good listener. Most health professionals today have very limited time to speak with their clients or answer questions. When people come to you, it will be a much needed breath of fresh air. They will be thrilled to have the space to speak about what is going on with their health and their life. By simply speaking and being listened to, the people who come to you for health histories will make connections around their health that they would not make if it were not for your presence.

What are five things that you already do that make you a good listener?

1. ....

2. ....

3. ....

4. ....

5. ....

INVITING PEOPLE TO A HEALTH HISTORY CONSULTATION

Coming to a health history consultation with you is a great opportunity for anyone. Remember to honor your worth when extending invitations. What you are offering is free, but it is incredibly valuable. Even if the person doesn't express interest in signing up for your program, simply talking about their health with you for an hour will be extremely beneficial.

Even though you may not be ready to see clients, start doing health history consultations now to get familiar with the process. It's best to do at least one or two a week. The first 10 you do will be the most difficult. So get the first 10 out of the way as soon as possible. Practicing health histories will build your confidence, and you will find your own unique style and become more comfortable with the process. Also, as you do more, the word will begin to spread about the new work you are doing.

LISTENING TIPS

Most people live in their heads, thinking about what they have to do tomorrow, what happened yesterday or an hour ago, pretty much anything except the present moment. Because we are all living in our own heads, we are rarely listening to what other people are saying. Likewise, it is rare that someone actually listens to us without interruption or judgment. When done well, listening delivers tremendous benefits.

As a Health Counselor, you are offering anyone who comes to you for a health history the priceless opportunity of being listened to. The more you develop your listening skills, the better a Health Counselor you will be.

In order to listen well, put all the thoughts about yourself out of your head. Focus on the person you are listening to. This will greatly improve the quality of your communication. Listening is an art that fosters understanding, affirmation, relatedness and appreciation.

Tips for Listening Well, Both on the Phone and in Person:

- Remain curious and ask pertinent questions that bring the person deeper into what they are talking about.
- Summarize what they say to determine if you accurately understand the speaker.
- In person, keep strong eye contact. On the phone, it's good to say things or make noises to let them know you are listening and comprehending what they are saying.
- Try to sit in one place. Avoid moving around.
- Learn to be comfortable with silence and being quiet. Don't talk in awkward silences; sometimes this is when the client reveals the most important information.
- Listen with your whole body: ears to hear the message, eyes to read body language (in person), the mind to visualize the person speaking (phone), intuition to determine what the speaker is actually saying.
- Meet in an environment conducive to listening. Avoid coffee or tea shops with loud music, tables that are very close together, or outside parks with a lot of children.

Things to Avoid When Listening:

- Looking at your watch or around the room instead of focusing on the speaker's face.
- Multitasking: Avoid writing a lot, cleaning, looking around for something, and cooking when you are meeting a client in person. If you are conducting the session over the phone, avoid opening mail, reading email, filing and playing with your hair or a pencil.
- Constantly interrupting, or finishing the other person's sentences.

As you are beginning your work and training as a Health Counselor, we recommend that you practice health histories with fellow students, instead of with family, friends, or people who may become clients. This will help you build your skills and your confidence and prepare you for even greater success when you do the consultation with potential clients. You can ask other students in class to practice with you, either by phone or in person. If you'd like, you can post on the OEF and ask who would be interested in practicing with you. An exciting part of being a Health Counselor is talking to strangers about what you do.

Potential clients are everywhere: at the health food store, the gym, yoga class, the bookstore, church, temple, on the bus, at the bank, everywhere! List five places that you know of where you think you could eventually find someone who would want to do a health history consultation with you. You can start going to these places now even just to say hello and build your contact list.

1. ....

2. ....

3. ....

4. ....

5. ....

You may be very comfortable talking to strangers, or you may not. If you don't, that's okay. You will learn. Start off slowly and build up your muscle for starting conversations with people.

COMMUNICATING WITH POTENTIAL CLIENTS

After you are familiar with the Health History Forms and you have a list of people to contact, you are ready to start inviting people for a free consultation. Once you are instructed to do so in class, you will start to contact other people besides fellow classmates. Please take a moment now to make a list of five people, other than classmates, whom you will do a health history with once instructed to do so. You can have this list ready to go once we provide additional instructions.

1. ....

2. ....

3. ....

4. ....

5. ....

For now, though, you can start building relationships, letting people (especially those on the above list) know what you are up to, and actually invite them for a health history later on (see Sample Email 1). Just keep in touch with them periodically by email or phone.

At this point in time you are not looking to actually get clients enrolled in a paid program; your goal is simply to practice health histories. In general, we recommend that you tell everyone you know what you are doing and once instructed to do so, invite them to come for a free health history (see Sample Email 2). Tell your friends, colleagues, acquaintances—everyone.

When it's time to start reaching out to other people in addition to your class mates, you can send out a professional, warm email to all of your contacts, inviting them to a health history. You can also send a casual email out to your close friends seeing whether they are interested, or whether they know someone who might be interested in doing a health history consultation with you.

If someone asks you what a health history is, you can say, "We will spend about an hour going through your Health History Form and discussing what you eat, your lifestyle and any goals for your health. We will also get a sense of how it would be to work together. How does that sound?"

Share how excited you are and how much your life has improved since changing your diet and lifestyle. You can give them an example of a health concern that you have cleared up or something that is going really well with you as a result of getting involved with the school and health counseling. This will inspire them to want to have more of what you have!

Here are some examples of what to say when inviting people for a health history consultation:

- "I am taking this course at a nutrition school in New York City, and I have a homework assignment to do some health history consultations. Would you be interested in sitting down with me for an hour while we discuss your health?"

- "Do you think you have an hour sometime this week to sit down with me and talk about your health? We can look at what you are eating and how that is affecting your health."

- "Have you ever thought about how what you eat affects your health? I'd be happy to talk with you about it further in a free consultation."

- "I have some exciting news. I am in school to become a certified Health Counselor. I'd love to show you what I'm learning. Would you like to sit down with me and discuss what is happening in your life and with your health?"

- "I am a student at the Institute for Integrative Nutrition in New York City, studying to be a certified Health Counselor. I am learning about how food, diet and lifestyle have a tremendous impact on our overall health, happiness and well-being. Not only am I learning to improve my life, I am also learning how to see clients and help them to reach their health goals and to feel and look better."

Notes:

- Ask the person, "I'm curious, what is one area of your health you would like to improve?" or "What is your main health concern?" After they respond, you can say something like, "Actually, part of my course requirements and homework are to do free health consultations with other people. I'd be happy to sit down with you and have a conversation about your health goals. Would you be interested in doing a health history consultation with me?"

- If inviting a person to do a health history is scary, you can practice telling people that you are studying to be a Health Counselor. From there, they will most likely ask what a Health Counselor is or what you are studying in school. You can tell them, "I help people discover how what they eat affects their health" or "I work with people to help them improve their diet and lifestyle."

- Listen to how they respond, and if it is positive, you can say, "Would you be interested in doing a free consultation with me?" Another approach to take is to talk to people about something you learned in class. For example, if you are in a social setting you can say, "Last weekend in class I heard from the head of nutrition at Harvard and he said . . ." From there, they may ask more about what you are studying. If they sound interested, you can invite them for a health history.

Be yourself. Say whatever is true for you. With time and practice, you will find your personal style and language.

Sample Email 1: Use this email to introduce your contacts to your health counseling training.

Subject: [   ]

Dear (name),

I have some exciting news! I am beginning a new business as a Health Counselor. I will be working with people on how to improve their diet and lifestyle. As you know, I have always had an interest in health (or nutrition or healing) and have enjoyed sharing this knowledge with my friends, colleagues and family. I decided that I wanted to increase this knowledge and learn, in a formal training program, how to live a better life through eating well and taking care of myself. I am currently enrolled at the Institute for Integrative Nutrition in New York City. I am not only learning how to take care of myself, I am also receiving very detailed and careful instruction on how to counsel others around food and lifestyle choices. It's an exciting time!

I look forward to sharing more with you about my new career path, and all of the benefits of this work. I'll be inviting people to health consultations in the near future, to have the opportunity to support them to create a happier, healthier and more fulfilling life. I'll be in touch periodically to let you know how my training is progressing. I appreciate being able to share this with you.

I hope you are well, and I wish you a great day! I look forward to talking with you soon.

Regards,
Counselor Name

Sample Email 2: Use this email to invite people to a health history.

Subject: [   ]

Hello, (name)!

I hope you are well, and that (personal note, e.g., "your husband Tom is doing well at his new job").

I am writing because I'm very excited to share something new and good that is happening in my life.

I recently decided to begin training in a new career path, and I enrolled at the Institute for Integrative Nutrition in New York City. I am learning to become a certified Health Counselor. As you know, I have always had an interest in health (or nutrition or healing) and have enjoyed sharing this knowledge with my friends, colleagues and family. I decided that I wanted to increase this knowledge and learn, in a formal training program, how to live a better life through eating well and taking care of myself. I am not only learning how to take care of myself, I am also receiving very detailed and careful instruction on how to counsel others around food and lifestyle choices. It's an exciting time!

Part of my course requirements and homework are to do free health consultations with other people.

I'd like to invite you to do a session with me. You'll have the opportunity to talk about your life, what you've always dreamed of, and the goals you'd like to accomplish. It's an opportunity to be heard and to get a sense of what it feels like to have more support in your life. And I'd be happy to have this time to share with and support you in living an even happier, healthier life. In this consultation, we will spend about an hour going through your Health History Form and your goals for your health. We will also get a sense of how it would be to work together once I am able to start seeing clients.

I'd appreciate being able to share this session with you and allow you to have time to talk about your health and life. The session is free and confidential and we can meet wherever it's convenient for you.

Please let me know what your schedule is like in the coming 1-2 weeks, and when you might have time to talk. Currently I have time available on (list two days/times). I will contact you again on (five days later) to follow up if we don't have a chance to speak before then.

I look forward to hearing from you, and I hope you have a great day.

Regards,
Counselor Name

SCHEDULING HEALTH HISTORY CONSULTATIONS

Read the next sentence very carefully. If someone expresses interest in doing a health history with you, schedule it on the spot! Set the exact time and place where the health history will be. You can say, "Great! I am free on Tuesday and Thursday nights and Sunday afternoons. Would any of those times work for you?" Or you might say something like, "I would love to set up a free consultation with you. My schedule can get full very quickly, so is it okay if we schedule it now? What days and times work best for you next week?"

This means you should start carrying a planner with you at all times, because you never know when you are going to meet potential clients. You also want to make sure you get the person's phone number and email. Let them know you will email them the details of when and where to meet you. Within 24 hours, email them the address, your phone number and the date and time of your appointment. You will also send them a reminder about your appointment 24 hours beforehand.

If you skip this crucial step of immediately scheduling appointments, you will lose out on potential clients. People are not going to knock down your door to schedule a health history with you. It's not because they don't want to work with you; it's because they are busy and they do not prioritize their health. They put their jobs, relationships and a million other things ahead of their own well-being. They need you to be the advocate for the importance of their health. You can do this for them by being assertive in scheduling the initial consultation. You are not doing anyone any favors by playing small or being shy.

If you don't have your schedule, or it's not an appropriate situation in which to schedule the health history, get the person's contact information and be in touch within 24 hours to set up the appointment.

FREQUENTLY ASKED QUESTIONS AND SUGGESTED ANSWERS

Sometimes, when scheduling a health history or during the actual consultation, people will ask you questions you may or may not have answers to. In these situations, it is best to answer the questions honestly. If you don't know the answer, you can say, "That's a great question, I will look into it and get back to you."

Also, you can practice ahead of time by anticipating potential questions and deciding on the best responses. You can also write down questions people ask you during the health history and keep a list of them for future reference.

What is a Health History?

"During a typical consultation, we will spend about an hour going through your Health History and your goals for your health, and what you've always imagined for your life. We will also get a sense of how it would be to work together. How does that sound?"

What is a Health Counselor?

"A Health Counselor guides you to reach your health and life goals by making step-by-step changes to your food and lifestyle, at a pace that's comfortable for you." If people who are not clients ask you for advice, try not to give them recommendations. Instead, say, "I just started my training program, and for now I'm not giving recommendations. That is a great question though, and those concerns you mentioned are the types of things we would cover together if you were to become my client."

Are you really qualified to see people before you finish your training?

"It is very common that other professionals like lawyers and psychologists to begin to see clients/patients before the end of their training, just like I do as a Health Counselor. This coming summer, I will be fully certified by the American Association of Drugless Practitioners."

What about confidentiality?

"Like any other health professional, I keep everything clients share with me strictly confidential."

How does the program work?

"I will be working with clients in six-month health counseling programs. During the six months, I will meet my clients individually twice a month and help them to reach their goals for their life and their health. Together, we will look at their current diet and lifestyle and customize a plan for how to upgrade their food and other aspects of their life. I will also offer cooking classes, a health food store tour, books and CDs on health-related topics and other fun ideas to help improve their health. Right now I am offering free initial consultations and I will begin to see clients in a few months."

Why is it six months?

"Studies show that if you do something for six months, it is likely to become a long-term habit. My goal is that after six months of working together with a client, they will have a deeper understanding of the foods and lifestyle that work best for them. I want them to take what they learn through working with me and use it for the rest of their life."

KEEPING TRACK OF CLIENTS

As you begin inviting people to health history consultations and lining up potential future clients, you will need a way to keep track of it all. At a minimum, we recommend that you keep track of the person's name, their email and phone numbers, the date of their health history consultation, and any relevant notes that you will want to remember. You will especially want to remember whether or not they are a potential client for you once you are ready to start seeing clients. We've included a sample Health History Tracking Form at the end of this chapter. You will also receive an electronic copy in class. You can edit it in any way that makes sense to you. The important thing is that you keep track.

HEALTH HISTORY EXCITEMENT

We understand that the idea of doing a health history with someone is a new concept for you. You probably have a myriad of different thoughts and emotions about this, from fear to excitement and nervousness.

List three things that you are nervous about:

1. ....

2. ....

3. ....

You can use your counselor, the OEF and your fellow students to help you work through anything that you are nervous about. Remember to feel the fear and do it anyway! We ask that instead of focusing on what is scary, you focus your attention on your excitement. In fact, all nervousness usually comes out of excitement. Allow yourself to be happily energized about this new adventure you are beginning.

List three things that are exciting regarding doing health histories:

1. ....

2. ....

3. ....

HEALTH HISTORY TRACKING FORM

Name	Phone	Email	Date of HH	Potential Client?	Follow-up Notes

GRADUATE PROFILE

FRANCES MURCHISON
Lake Forest, IL
frances@mindfullyfed.com
2003 Graduate

I worked in advertising in New York City for 15 years before I came to Integrative Nutrition. I enjoyed what I was doing, but I was exhausted from working 15-hour days, and I wanted to be home with my kids. Food was always important to me, as was feeding my kids really well.

As soon as I entered the doors of Integrative Nutrition, I knew I wanted to make a career out of health counseling. My goal from day one was to make my tuition investment back by the time I finished the program. It was a great motivator for me to get my business started.

The biggest step I took to build my practice while in school was affiliating with an integrative medical practice. I met one of the doctors through a friend of a friend and invited her to have lunch with me. I asked her to seriously consider having me in the office. I explained to her that it was a win/win proposition. She would make money by renting space to me, and it would give her the credibility of having a truly integrated practice by adding a nutrition expert to her staff.

She agreed! I graduated the program with 15 clients, and about half of them were referrals from the doctors there. I moved to Chicago shortly after graduation and found myself having to start all over again. I didn't know a soul, so I decided I would make some friends with people who had lived in the area for a long time and offer free cooking classes to their contact lists. I met one friend who was willing to provide me with the names and addresses of 50 people in the area. I sent them all hard-copy invitations to a cooking class, and about 30 people accepted. Five people signed up for my program. I continued setting up paid cooking class series and other group events, and within six months I had 15 clients!

> "For the first time in my life, I feel like I am doing what I am meant to be doing."

I recommend that you make it a point to tell at least three people each day what you're doing. The more people you tell, the more you will believe in yourself and get comfortable in your new role as a Health Counselor. Another tip is to stick to the policy of having clients pay up-front. When I first started, I bent over backwards to accommodate people because I was afraid they would say no to my program. The more I set boundaries and raised my rates, the more people wanted my service.

I learned everything I know about building a business at Integrative Nutrition. I had always dreamed of being an entrepreneur, but I was scared to death, so I stayed in my corporate job. For the first time in my life, I feel like I am doing what I am meant to be doing. I have finally figured out how to take my wisdom and experience and offer it back to the world.

*Pleasure in the job puts
perfection in the work.*

—Aristotle

CHAPTER 3:

THE BUILDING BLOCKS FOR A BUSINESS

O nce you've completed several health histories and have a clear idea of what health counseling is, you are ready to set up your business. Having a legitimate business will help you look and feel more professional. It is also important to officially start your own business so that you will be in adherence with any business laws in your state. Please keep in mind, though, you can start your marketing efforts before you set up your business officially.

For many of you, running your own business may be a lifelong dream. In this chapter, we'll review some basic steps for getting your business up and running, including creating your office, determining your business name and your title, picking a legal structure, how to register, creating a website, setting up bank accounts, accepting credit cards and managing finances.

This book cannot substitute for the legal, financial and other professional advice required when establishing or expanding a business. While every effort has been made to ensure that the information included in this book is accurate, we urge you to consult with your state's appropriate agencies and work with a qualified professional before actually proceeding to establish a business.

FORMS

All of the forms you will need to run your health counseling practice will be provided throughout the school year. You should save each to your computer and spend some time reviewing everything that is on it. You can also customize the forms as you see fit, adding your logo, name or contact information.

You may want to print out some forms and have on hand, such as the Health History Forms, Program Agreement and any other forms that you use on a regular basis. One suggestion is to have client folders ready to go, each containing a blank Health History Form,

Program Agreement, Client Progress Form and Giveaway Checklist. This way when you have a health history you just grab one of the folders, rather than printing out and organizing all the paperwork each time.

You may want to staple the Client Progress Form to the left side of the folder and the Giveaway Checklist to the right side. After each session, you can easily mark down how the session went and what you gave to your client. If you can find a way that works for you to organize all your forms and paperwork, it will save you a lot of time and stress in the future.

OFFICE SET-UP

When you first begin health counseling, it's completely okay for you to not have an office. You can meet your clients in a coffee shop, library, bookstore, their home, your home or a hotel lobby. Any place has advantages and disadvantages. You will want to meet your clients in a comfortable setting where you can speak about personal topics.

Eventually you will want to get office space. An office space will allow you to stay in one place to see your clients, and guarantee that you have the exact environment you want. You may rent an office or create one in your home.

If you choose to rent an office, consider renting in a massage therapy practice, a wellness center or a therapist's office with other health professionals who might refer clients to you. You can also rent space from community centers, YMCAs and churches at reasonable rates. Some Health Counselors get together in groups of two to four and rent a single office, splitting the rent to make it more affordable.

If you use your home as your office, it's helpful to pick an area of your house where you will see clients. It may be at your kitchen table or on your couch. Perhaps you have a room that you can turn into your office. If you don't have an area that works, think about purchasing Japanese screens and sectioning off a small area of your home where you can fit two chairs and a small table. You'll need at least two comfortable chairs in your office. You'll also need a clock, strategically placed so that you can easily view it during your sessions and keep track of time. You may also want to have attractive decorations, a hot pot for making tea, a CD player to play relaxing music and a bookshelf to display all of your books. You will also need office space to do all of your paperwork and correspondence. This may or may not be the same place where you see your clients. For more office supplies you may need, please refer back to Chapter 1: "Starting on Your Road to Success," page 3.

CREATING A BUSINESS NAME

There is no "one-size-fits-all" formula for picking a fantastic business name. But you can consider a few things, such as the kind of business you do, your target market and your unique style or personality. Your business name should be distinctive and memorable, suggest the services you offer, and be easy to spell and pronounce.

The options for your business name are endless. You can use your first or last name as part of it, which is recommended, such as Jane Smith Health or Health with Jane. Or, you can pick a powerful name that conveys what your business is about without including your name. Words such as "health," "nurturing" and "wellness" are popular among our students and graduates.

Write six possible business names here:

1. Create Your Life   CrEATe Your Life
2.
3.
4.
5.
6.

crEATe your life

Which of these names best represents what you do? What sounds the strongest to you? If you are not sure, you can ask your friends, family, fellow students and Health Counselor what they think.

We suggest you give yourself a few weeks before finalizing your decision and registering your business name. Make sure that someone else does not already have the rights to use the name you have chosen. Remember, though, the most important part of your business is you. Your energy and enthusiasm will speak louder than your business name.

Here are steps you can take in conducting a name search:

1. A quick and easy place to start is with an online search engine, such as Google. When you Google the name you like, what else comes up? Is there clearly another business with this name?

2. Go to godaddy.com or networksolutions.com and type, in the domain name search option, the name you want to use. If another company has reserved a domain name that contains the business name you want, you probably won't be able to use it because the domain name qualifies as a trademark if the website is used commercially.

3. Get in touch with your county clerk's office. There you can check a list of all the assumed business names in the country. In some states, you can also check with the state corporation commission to view a database of all business names.

4. If someone else is using the business name you want to use, you shouldn't use it. You might also want to check that your business name can be used as a website address, also called a domain name or URL. These days, most successful businesses have websites. Having your website match your business name allows potential clients to find you quickly and easily. For example, if your business name is "Health with Jane," you might want to use healthwithjane.com as your domain name. It can be difficult to find a domain name that is not already taken.

YOUR TITLE

We think that the term "Health Counselor" is the most accurate description of what our students and graduates practice with their clients. Your Integrative Nutrition diploma will say that you are a certified Health Counselor. After graduation you can put HC (Health Counselor) after your name. However, you do not have to use this title. Some graduates choose to call themselves holistic Health Counselors, health coaches or lifestyle coaches. It's up to you.

Be careful, however, about picking titles that require certain qualifications that you do not have. For example, you cannot call yourself a registered dietician in any of the states unless you are registered with the American Dietetic Association. Also, if you decide to use the term "coach," you cannot call yourself certified. Most states also have strict guidelines on who can use the term "nutritionist."

DETERMINING YOUR BUSINESS STRUCTURE AND REGISTERING YOUR BUSINESS

Once you choose your business name and title, you can register your business so that you are in adherence with state or local regulations in your area. The process of registering your company with your state and local governments will vary depending on the business entity type. This section describes the most common forms of business entities. All this business information may seem overwhelming at this time. Breathe. And read each section slowly and carefully. We will talk about this more in class to provide any additional support. We included it here to give you a clear picture of your options.

SOLE PROPRIETORSHIPS

Most new businesses, and most students at Integrative Nutrition, start as sole proprietorships because it is the easiest, cheapest and quickest way to create a business. In fact, about 70 percent of small businesses are sole proprietorships. This type of business is an option if you are going to be the only person who owns the business. If you have co-owners or partners, sole proprietorships are not allowed, unless your partner is your spouse.

A sole proprietorship is a business that is owned by one individual, and is unincorporated. This is the simplest form of business organization to start and maintain. In a sole proprietorship, the business and its owner are one and the same. The business has no existence apart from you, the owner. Therefore, you are solely responsible for your business and any liabilities are your personal liabilities. The record keeping is very simple because your business doesn't have to file income tax returns or pay income taxes. All the money that is made is considered your income. If you are sole proprietor you don't need a federal identification number for your business, so you may use your social security number.

Sole proprietorships are so easy to set up and maintain that you may already own one without knowing it. If you are a freelance writer, a massage therapist who is not on an employer's payroll or a salesperson who receives only commissions, you are already a sole proprietor. Even though a sole proprietorship is easy to start and maintain, you may have to comply with local registration, business license or permit laws to make your business legitimate.

LIMITED LIABILITY COMPANIES (LLCS)

In order to create an LLC, most states require two owners, who can be spouses. An LLC is set up like a sole proprietorship in that all the profits go directly to the owners, but there is a distinction between the owners and the business, protecting the owners from any personal liability. The paperwork for creating an LLC is less complex than for a corporation, but more complex than for a sole proprietorship. Go to llc.com for more thorough information.

CORPORATIONS

Corporations provide a business entity that is separate from the owner as an individual. It can be expensive to start a corporation, but the owner avoids liability. Minimum requirements for maintaining a corporation include conducting annual meetings, filing minutes in your corporate books and filing the required documentation with the state on an annual basis. While double taxation is sometimes mentioned as a drawback to incorporation, the S corporation (or Subchapter corporation, a popular variation of the regular C corporation) avoids this situation by allowing income or losses to be passed through on individual tax returns, similar to a partnership. The main reason for incorporating is to limit your personal liability. You would pay yourself a salary.

SETTING UP A SOLE PROPRIETORSHIP

Unless you have a strong business background and are up for the task of creating a corporation or LLC, we recommend starting your business as a sole proprietorship. You can always transition to another kind of business structure in the future, but for your first year as a Health Counselor, a sole proprietorship will likely provide you with everything you need.

After you have made certain the business and domain names you want are available, you may fill out a simple "Doing Business As" (DBA) form with your local government. A DBA is a business filing that allows business owners to operate a company under a name other than their own name at a minimal cost. In most states, if your business is your first and last name, such as Jane Smith Health or Healing with Jane Smith, a DBA is not required. However, if you want your business to be called "Holistic Healing," you will need a DBA since that business name is not your legal name (Jane Smith).

Having a DBA allows you to use a name without filing a legal entity, such as a corporation, partnership or LLC. It also protects the business name from being used by anyone else. Most states and counties require that you file a DBA to legally run a business by a name other than your own, even a small home run-business. Also, banks won't let you open a business account unless you have registered your business name.

Filing a DBA is simple and takes little time. First, call your county clerk's office to learn about the local fees and procedures in your area. They can tell you where to get the DBA form, also called an Assumed Business Name Form, and where to submit it. Follow the instructions provided by the county clerk, and submit the proper form and filing fee. Once your DBA filing is approved, you will get your Business Certificate and your business is officially registered.

Some states, such as California, also require that you publish an announcement in a local newspaper with your business name. Please check in with your local county clerk's office, either in person or on the web, to read more about the regulations in your state.

OBTAINING A FEDERAL IDENTIFICATION NUMBER

If you set your business up as a corporation, partnership or LLC, you will need to obtain a federal identification number. When you research how to register your business in your state, you will probably find instructions on how to do this. But in case you don't, you can simply fill out Form SS-4, Application for Employer Identification Number, available at www.irs.gov/pub/irs-pdf/fss4.pdf, and mail or fax it to the IRS Service Center in your state. You can also apply by phone by calling 1-800-829-3676.

You will not need a federal identification number if you are setting up your business as a sole proprietorship. As mentioned above, your social security number will serve as your ID. The government assigns federal identification numbers in order to keep track of small businesses for tax, budget and census purposes.

SATISFYING ALL STATE AND LOCAL REQUIREMENTS

Once you have registered your business and, if necessary, gotten a federal identification number, you will need to make sure that you are complying with all state and local requirements for running a business. For example, you may need to purchase a business license from your county. Your county's website will most likely have the information you need to make sure you are complying with county requirements, and you can use your state website to find out how to satisfy state requirements.

Notes:

SETTING UP A DOMAIN NAME

Next, you will want to make it easy for potential clients to find you. As an Integrative Nutrition student, you will automatically receive your own beautiful website with information about your program offerings. This saves you the expense of designing a website. We will host this website for free for at least one year after you graduate. The address of your website will be something like: www.websites.integrativenutrition.com/YOURUSERNAME/index.aspx. If you want to have a different web address, or if you want to create your own, you will have to purchase a domain name from a provider and have it routed to your Integrative Nutrition-provided page.

If you decide to purchase your own URL, we suggest that you go to www.startlogic.com, www.register.com, www.godaddy.com or any of the more reliable web domain and hosting companies and follow the instructions there. They have services that will allow you to direct your Integrative Nutrition-provided website to the name you choose.

If buying a domain name at this time feels like too much work, you do not have to do it. Your efforts are better spent working towards doing health history consultations and building your name in your community and with your target market. Do not waste time figuring out how to build a complex website before you have your first five clients.

 RESOURCE GUIDE

Your state's website will have information on how to select a business structure as well as the specific regulations for each option in your area. Visit the website (e.g.,www.state.ny.us, www.ct.gov, www.newjersey.gov) and search in the "Business" section.

You can also contact the U.S. Small Business Association website at www.sba.gov for more information on the advantages and disadvantages of each business entity mentioned above, and to find a Small Business Association in your area.

Other local assistance options include Small Business Development Centers, Service Corps of Retired Executives (SCORE), Veterans Business Outreach Centers and Women's Business Centers. You can also contact your local Chamber of Commerce, which has many options to support business owners. Look in your local phone book for any of these organizations.

You may also want to consult with an accountant, lawyer or anyone else you know who is knowledgeable about your state's laws and your personal situation.

If you happen to be a web designer or know someone who would do this for you at minimal cost, then it may be worth it.

BUSINESS BANK ACCOUNT

We find it helpful to separate your business and personal finances. Some small business owners pay their expenses out of personal accounts and deposit business income and income from other sources into family checking accounts that are shared with a spouse. While this may be okay in the beginning, as you grow your business, not having one bank account for business and one for personal or family expenses can create complications.

For example, if you do business under a name other than your own, your bank may not allow you to deposit checks that are made out to your company name. And if you have your business money in a joint account with someone else, what happens if you have to write a check for your business the same day your husband, wife or partner drew on that same money for something else the same day? Also, if you keep your business money in your personal account, when it comes time to do taxes, it will be more difficult to figure out your deductions, fees, expenses and so on.

As mentioned earlier, if you have a sole proprietorship, your money and the business's money are one and the same. It is not necessary for you to keep a separate account, but it can be helpful. If you keep your business finances separate from your personal finances you can put all the money you make from health counseling into a different account and pay all your business expenses from the same account. Having a separate business account will ensure that you keep track of how much money you are putting into and getting out of your business. It will also help you when it comes time to do your taxes.

Once you register your business, you will get an official Business Certificate and you will be able to open a business bank account. If you set up as a sole proprietor and get a DBA, you will have your Business Certificate when you leave the county clerk's office. Most banks require that you have a Business Certificate to open a business bank account.

Many banks offer free checking for small business owners. You can also usually get a no-fee debit or credit card. Figure out how many deposits and how many payments you expect to make a week. Chances are it will only be a few per week, in which case you will be able to get a low-cost or free bank account. A basic plan usually has unlimited checking each month.

Find a reputable bank that you have used in the past. It's probably easiest to use the same bank you use for your personal account if it has a business branch. You can call them, schedule a visit or drop in to find out what your options are when it comes to small business bank accounts. In order to open a business bank account, you will need the following documentation:

- Your federal identification number (if you are a sole proprietorship, that's your own social security number).
- A photo ID (either a driver's license or a passport).
- Your business certificate.

ACCEPTING PAYMENTS

Most of our students are very skilled counselors; they are great listeners who are intuitive and genuinely enjoy talking to people. Counseling is the easy part for them. The hardest part is asking their clients for money. We will be examining this more thoroughly in Chapter 5.

To help you overcome any fear about asking people to pay you, we are going to be very clear about the different options you have when it comes to getting paid. Do you want your clients to pay in full up-front or in monthly installments; or use cash, check or credit card?

GETTING PAID UP-FRONT VS. IN MONTHLY INSTALLMENTS

Of course, it is always exciting to get paid in full at the beginning of your program. When you first start out as a Health Counselor, you may keep your fees a little lower as you get your feet wet. So paying in full may be quite doable for your clients.

As you get more experience and raise your rates, your clients may want to pay in monthly installments. We'll discuss how to price your program in Chapter 5, but to get started we generally recommend charging around $75 to 95 per month as a student, and $195 per month once you graduate. You might consider encouraging your clients to pay in full by offering them a discount for doing so. For example, "save 10 percent if you pay in full" or "get $100 off the full price if you pay in full."

Some graduates actually prefer to have their clients pay in monthly installments. This helps them with budgeting. Also, the monthly payments help them stay motivated and interested in their clients. If your client pays in monthly installments, you will need to set up a system for keeping track of the payments. An example of a very simple system is on the next page:

MONTHLY PAYMENT FORM

Client	Month 1	Month 2	Month 3	Month 4	Month 5	Month 6	TOTAL
	Type	Type	Type	Type	Type	Type	
eg., Jane Smith	$195/ credit card						

As you get new clients, simply add them to the list, and then enter each payment into the appropriate cell. Using this system, you will know how much you've earned each month, and at the end of the year you can easily tally the total income you've earned.

CASH, CHECK OR CREDIT CARD

Cash: Everyone likes to get paid in cash. However, if you are not skilled at money management, this may not be the best way for you to get paid. Cash is easy to spend because it goes into your wallet and you forget that it was your paycheck from your client. Also, if your rates go up, it may not be feasible or convenient for your clients to pay you in cash. If your client wants to pay with cash, they should pay up-front. If they say they will pay you in cash each month, you will have to remember to ask them for the money at each session. You don't want to be discussing money during the program. You want them to pay you in full up-front, give you post-dated checks or give you a credit card that you will charge each month.

Check: Checks are a great way to get paid. Unlike credit cards, you will not have to pay a fee for accepting a check as payment. We highly suggest that you ask your clients who want to pay you by check to give you six post-dated checks—one for each month you will be working together. That way, you will not have to ask your client for payment each month, freeing you up to focus on your work as a Health Counselor. Have your client date the checks for the same date of every month. The 1st and the 15th are usually the most convenient. Once you receive the checks, be sure to keep them in a safe place. Keeping checks from all clients for a certain date in one convenient spot will make your bank runs easier. It is good customer service to deposit checks within three days of their date.

Credit Cards: Credit cards are very convenient for your clients and will allow you to easily process payments, but there is a fee. This is also great when working with phone clients. The easiest way to accept credit cards is to use PayPal. This lets you accept credit cards, bank transfers, debit cards and more—at some of the lowest costs in the industry. Plus, your customers can pay you instantly, even if they don't have a PayPal account, via American Express, MasterCard, Visa, Discover and debit cards. You do not need to pay any set-up or cancellation fees, and you get transaction rates around 2.9 percent + $0.30 per transaction. See www.paypal.com for details.

Another way to accept credit cards is to set up a merchant account through your bank. If you already have a business account, your bank may be able to help you accept credit cards as well.

CREDIT CARD AUTHORIZATION FORM

CREDIT CARD AUTHORIZATION FORM

I, _____, hereby authorize _____ to charge the following credit card account in the amount shown below for monthly health counseling services. This payment agreement will be in effect until services have been completed or are ended by request of the client either verbally or in writing.

CREDIT CARD INFORMATION:

Card Type: VISA _____ MASTERCARD _____

Card Number:	_____
Expiration Date:	_____
Name on Card:	_____
Billing Street Address:	_____
City, State, Zip:	_____
Email Address:	_____

Amount	$	per month for 6 months = $	TOTAL

Cardholder's Signature: ....

Thank you.

Finally, many of our graduates who have many clients use www.practicepaysolutions.com to set up an online account that accepts credit cards. With Practice Pay Solutions (PPS), you simply collect the credit card information from your client, log into the PPS website and enter in the information to charge the client. The money is then transferred from the client's credit card directly into your business bank account. If you choose this route, take a look at the Credit Card Authorization Form we've included above. Also, PPS gives Integrative Nutrition students a discount. We will be talking about this more in class.

MANAGING FINANCES

A critical part of running a business successfully is having a system and structure in place for managing your finances. This step is important for tax purposes, making financial decisions, collecting payments and projecting financial goals long term. Poor financial planning will decrease your income and will jeopardize the success of your business. Accounting is simply a process of tracking what you spend and what you make.

STEPS FOR FINANCIAL PLANNING:

Step 1: Set Up a System to Track Your Finances

As mentioned, opening a separate account allows you to easily keep track of your finances. You can: use a spreadsheet or database program on your PC or Mac, keep a ledger and record manually, or purchase a software system, like Quicken or QuickBooks.

Keep on top of this work. You should plan to spend time each week updating your records. It is also important that you keep all of your receipts and tax forms from year to year, since you could be asked by the IRS to show proof of your earnings and expenses.

Step 2: Track Your Expenses

A great thing about health counseling is that you won't have many large expenses. No inventory, no employees. The biggest expense you will have is rent, if you are renting an office space, and your client giveaways. We suggest that you spend approximately 10 percent of your client revenue on giveaways. So if your client is paying you $200 per month, you have $20 each month to spend on gifts.

Per tax regulations, you are eligible to deduct expenses for your business from your income. These expenses must be "incurred in connection with your business, ordinary (similar to others in your field), and necessary." Basically, any money you spend to run your business can be deducted, either in whole or by a percentage. Your accountant will know the specifics.

You should track all items, whether you paid cash, check or credit card. Keep every receipt, and organize them by category in a large manila or accordion envelope. If you don't have a receipt, record the amount, item and date with whatever system you have in place.

These are the types of expenses you may want to include:

- All goods you purchase for clients including: books, CDs, DVDs, food samples, self-care items.
- Office equipment including: computer, fax, copy machine, phone, chairs, table, frames, plants, lighting.
- Business use of home or rental office. You are entitled to deduct the percentage you actually use for seeing clients and running your business.
- Business supplies: paper, CD-ROMs, pens, files.
- Email, internet and computer costs.
- Phone bill. You may deduct a percentage, based on how much you use your phone for business.
- Marketing and promotion: ads, flyers, brochures, networking event fees, business cards, website creation, designer fees, hiring people.
- Renters and liability insurance.

Notes:

- Legal and professional services.

- Continuing education, including: workshops, seminars, events related to your field, learning a complementary modality. Find out from your accountant what is legal.

- If you take your clients to dinner or to an event, you can deduct a certain percentage of that expense.

- Event expenses for clients, including: the cost to rent a room for a workshop or food purchased for a cooking class.

- Transportation and lodging, including: speaking engagements, out-of-state conferences or business meetings.

- Association fees, including The American Association for Drugless Practitioners.

- Bank fees.

- If you rent or use your own car, you can deduct a certain percentage for gas and mileage based on how much you use it for business.

- If you rent an apartment and your office is in your home, a percentage of your rent may be deductible.

In terms of what you spend on Integrative Nutrition tuition, tax law states that education expenses incurred to change careers are not deductible. Education expenses that are extending your knowledge of your current profession are deductible, based on IRS guidelines. Again, your accountant will know what and how much you can claim as expenses.

Step 3: Track Your Revenue

You should record all income you earn related to your business—cash, check and credit card payments.

Types of revenue from health counseling:

- Client fees from your program
- Speaking engagements
- Group program revenue
- Corporate workshops
- Income from writing
- Consulting income
- Any products you sell
- Referral fees given to you by other practitioners

Track this revenue in your ledger or with your software or Excel, organizing it by month and by client. Using a software program makes it much easier to add, analyze the figures, and have a detailed and organized record to give to your accountant. If you have other income from your day job, you should also keep accurate records for this and provide all of the income to your accountant, who will be able to properly prepare your tax forms.

Step 4: File Your Taxes

We recommend that you set aside 30 percent of your income for taxes. For example, if you collect $200 from a client, set aside $60 for taxes. It is important to note that the tax laws are very complicated. And while this book is meant to provide an overview of financial planning, it is not meant to take the place of a qualified accountant. By spending money on an accountant, you actually save money, since he or she will know exactly how to provide the greatest savings for you and your business. Being self-employed means that you have the chance to keep a large percentage of what you make, since you are allowed to deduct expenses for your business. And tax laws are designed to support businesses. If you really don't want to hire an accountant, you can purchase tax preparation software, such as TurboTax.

MONEY PERSONALITIES

Usually when people go into business for themselves, issues about money come up. After all, this may be the first time in your life when you are directly asking people to pay you for your time. Please know that what you are offering your clients is incredibly valuable, and you deserve to get paid well for it. It's important to be clear on your ideas about money so that you do not create blocks for yourself when it comes time to get paid. When people pay for something they tend to value it more. Additionally, if you are earning a good income, you have the flexibility to do more not-for-profit work, as you are meeting your financial needs through paying clients.

MONEY BELIEF SYSTEM:

What are your earliest memories of money?

....

....

....

....

....

What were/are your parents' views of money?

....

....

....

What do you enjoy about money?

....

....

....

....

What difficulty do you have around money?

....

....

....

....

What is your current relationship with money?

....

....

....

....

For further reading about issues with money, we recommend *Creating True Prosperity,* by Shakti Gawain, New World Library, $13.95, and *Secrets of the Millionaire Mind,* by T. Harv Eker, $14.93.

PROFESSIONAL LIABILITY INSURANCE

Be sure to have all your clients sign the legal waiver that we provide you. After you graduate, you may want to purchase professional liability insurance if you can afford to do so. Prices may range from $250 to $500 per year. After you graduate, you can become a member of The American Association for Drugless Practitioners and purchase practice insurance from them (www.aadp.net).

We have never heard of any of our graduates needing professional liability insurance, and you can legally practice without it. Whether or not you purchase it is up to you.

Along with professional liability insurance you may also consider carrying disability insurance in the event you were sick or hurt, and not able to work and pay your business expenses or earn income. Given that most home business owners are sole proprietors, this type of insurance would, depending on the particular provider, give additional

TYPICAL MONEY PERSONALITIES

Throughout the years, we have identified that our students fall into different categories in terms of their relationships with money. Take a moment to see which one you identify with. Get support around letting go of any troubled past with money and recognizing that you can have a future full of abundance and wealth.

The Under-Earner: These people charge nothing, or very little for services. They believe this should be free to everyone. They usually ask for about $25 per month for their six-month program. These students have a hard time raising their rates and asking clients for money.

The Over-Giver: These people doubt their abilities as Health Counselors and make up for their insecurities by over-giving. They often spend a lot of money on giveaways and food, and their sessions usually go longer than the allotted hour. They spend a lot of what they earn on their clients and end up with little profit.

The Over-Spender: These people wish to portray themselves as successful. They spend lots of money on upscale offices and expensive clothes to help themselves feel professional and cover insecurities about doing this work.

In all of these cases, remember that your financial health and your belief in your own self-worth are tremendously important. The truth is, however you approach money in your career is how you look at it in all areas of your life. If you take this opportunity now to form a healthy, balanced relationship with money, it will change your life. By keeping yourself financially healthy, stress is usually reduced, which contributes to your overall health and happiness.

security. There are basically two types of disability insurance, short-term and long-term. Short-term typically has a limit to the length and amount of benefits you receive. Long-term tends to provide extended benefits, but may have a longer waiting period before actual initiation. For more information regarding disability insurance go to, www.about-disability-insurance.com. You can also contact your current insurance provider to inquire about their types of policies and coverage.

CHECK-IN

We've just given you a lot of new information about how to start a business as a Health Counselor. The next chapters will show you how to get out there, sign clients and be successful. Right now you may be feeling excited or nervous, overwhelmed or confident. Wherever you are is totally fine. Remember to stay focused, follow our instructions and ask for support when you need it.

Notes:

Take a minute to check in with yourself. How are you feeling about your business? What have you accomplished so far? What has been the most challenging part? What are you most looking forward to?

....

....

....

....

....

....

GRADUATE PROFILE

LARRY ROGOWSKY
Bronx, NY
larryrogo@hotmail.com
2006 Graduate

The whole concept of building your business while still in school is brilliant. I really encourage you to start your business now while you have tons of support so you can be on track when you graduate. It's important to take consistent action. Set attainable goals, make a clear plan to achieve them and take small steps daily.

> "I am making a real difference in peoples' lives by being myself..."

Because my office is located in the theater district, I work with many performers, as well as busy professionals. I help them to slow down, take time to eat and take care of themselves. I teach my clients to choose foods that give them the sustainable energy their lifestyle demands. I work with them to achieve optimal health and be the best they can be at all times.

Before I came to Integrative Nutrition, I was an actor turned massage therapist. I wanted to add another dimension to my massage practice, where I could use my mind and voice rather than just my physical body. Also, my massage clients were always asking me health-related questions. I wanted to give them answers and get paid for my expertise.

Adding health counseling to my massage practice was easy. I offered all of my clients free health histories, and many of them signed up for my six-month program. I also invited friends, family and everyone I met for health histories. People were genuinely interested and eager to hear more about what I do.

A month before graduation I had four clients, and I set a goal to have more before the school year ended. Within weeks of setting my goal, I had three more clients. The school gave me the motivation, support and skills to make it happen.

My first few health counseling clients have spread the word about me, so my business is growing mainly through referrals. Health counseling re-energized my massage practice too. I enjoy massage more, now that it is not the only work that I am doing.

Now that I'm cooking and eating whole foods, my own health is much better, my energy is great, and I'm inspiring my friends and my partner. Life has changed on many levels. I've met incredible people and have built really strong relationships.

I love that we are on the cutting edge of the health industry. I am making a real difference in peoples' lives by being myself and using my strengths of humor, care and love. I have the freedom to be flexible and put my personality into this work. I love sharing information and ideas and empowering my clients to decide for themselves the choices that are right for them.

*In order to succeed,
your desire for success should be
greater than your fear of failure.*

—Bill Cosby

CHAPTER 4:

FINDING AND KEEPING CLIENTS

Many of our graduates have enough clients that they need to hire additional Health Counselors to help counsel all of their clients. Wouldn't it be great if you were attracting so many clients you didn't know what to do with all of them? In order for you to get to this point, you have to put in a lot of work and practice doing health histories, workshops, marketing and networking. Even if you think you are not good at it or don't like marketing yourself, this chapter—and the curriculum taught in class—will support you in finding ways of marketing yourself that best suit you. Once you figure out how to attract the clients you want, you will be able to focus on building your business.

TARGET MARKET

In the early stages of health counseling, we recommend you do health histories with almost anyone who is interested and could be a good client, excluding those who are obviously problematic or suffering from life-threatening illnesses. As you do health histories with all different types of people, you will naturally start to identify those who are attracted to you and whom you most enjoy working with. For example, maybe you notice you really enjoy working with new moms. From there, you can narrow your marketing efforts to focus on setting up health histories with new moms. You can ask yourself, "Where can I go to meet this group? What are their concerns? How can I create an email or flyer that will address those issues?" New moms then become your target market. Other target markets might be busy executives, college students, marathon runners, yoga instructors or people with a specific health concern (such as celiac disease, Candida, migraines, sleep problems, stress or weight-loss).

Notes:

BENEFITS TO HAVING A CLEAR TARGET MARKET:

- Easier to market your services when you know whom you are trying to reach.
- You also can become an expert in a few particular health concerns, rather than learning about new health concerns with each new client.
- People seek health practitioners who are experts in their health concern.
- You will enjoy health counseling more if you are working with people who are interesting to you.
- People in this target market most likely know a lot of other people like themselves who will also be ideal clients for you.

Answer these questions to help you identify your target market:

1. What health or life issues are you working on or have you worked through? Your own experience and expertise may make you a perfect Health Counselor for people who are experiencing something you've already been through.

....

....

....

....

....

....

2. What type of person would you take pleasure in working with? Perhaps you've noticed in your health histories so far that a particular type of person really connects well with you, and you with them. You can list a few different types of people here. Get as specific as you can, e.g., women with eating disorders, single dads, twenty-somethings who live in New York City, women going through menopause, people with diabetes, children ages six to 10 or corporate professionals.

....

....

....

....

....

....

3. Out of these groups, who can afford your six-month program fee?

....

....

....

....

....

....

4. Now that you have identified people whom you would like to work with and who can afford your services? For example, working mothers may spend time at day care, or be involved with working mom groups or school functions. You can go to the places where your target client hangs out and share with people what you do as a Health Counselor. (See information on networking later in this chapter.)

....

....

....

....

....

....

5. What are the characteristics and qualities of people in your target market?

Age range: ....

Male or female: ....

Education level: ....

Career: ....

Income: ....

What are their needs, concerns and goals? ....

Who else serves these people? ....

Once you have identified the type of people you are trying to reach, you can narrow your networking and marketing efforts. This allows you to more effectively design and write your materials, as well as improve how you communicate what you do.

Notes:

DYNAMIC INTRODUCTION

As you probably already know, one of the basic steps to getting clients is to clearly communicate what you do. After all, how can people become clients if they don't know what you do? You should be able to summarize everything that you do in one or two sentences. This is what we call your "elevator speech." Here is the formula for a powerful elevator speech:

My name is ....

I am a Health Counselor. I work with ....

who ....

The first blank is your name, obviously. The second blank is your target market. The third blank is what you help your target market with.
Examples:

1. My name is Jane Smith. I work with young professionals who want help to reduce their stress and have more energy.

2. My name is Jane Smith. I work with busy moms who are struggling with preparing quick, healthy, enjoyable meals for their families, while also making sure they are taking care of themselves and their own health.

3. My name is Jane Smith. I work with men who are addicted to sugar to help them reduce their sugar cravings, have more energy and incorporate delicious, healthy foods into their diets.

This elevator speech should be your first step in introducing yourself to someone. During any conversation, you should be sure to listen and have the communication flow. Don't talk too much or try to say everything that you do in less than one minute. Share, ask questions and be genuinely interested in other people. Think about how you can explain your work in a way that is easy for them to understand and so they recognize the benefits of what you do. And always remember to get the person's contact information so you can add them to your mailing list.

COMPANY MISSION STATEMENT

After you've identified your target market, you can develop a mission statement for your business. A mission statement is a sentence, bullet points or paragraph illustrating the goals and purpose of your business. It's the vision of your company put into words.

Your mission statement should state your company's purpose. Have a central theme that is accurate and succinct. Be sure to include a description of the services offered along with who your target market is. Your mission statement should also focus on a few key attributes of your services.

Example:

Jane Smith Health provides busy moms with support in maintaining a healthy family and a high level of self-care. As a Health Counselor, my mission is to improve the health and happiness of my clients.

Use this space to write a first draft of your company mission statement. This is just a first draft; it doesn't need to be perfect. You can always refine it as your business grows.

....

....

....

....

....

....

Use this mission to guide you. This will be a powerful motivational tool for you, keeping you clear about the bigger picture of why you are doing what you are doing and what is driving you to accomplish your goals. Whenever you are unsure what steps to take with

MISSION STATEMENTS

Disney: To make people happy.

FedEx: FedEx is committed to our People-Service-Profit Philosophy. We will produce outstanding financial returns by providing totally reliable, competitively superior, global, air-ground transportation of high-priority goods and documents that require rapid, time-certain delivery.

Google: Google's mission is to organize the world's information and make it universally accessible and useful.

Institute for Integrative Nutrition: Our mission is to play a crucial role in improving the health and happiness in America, and through that process, create a ripple effect that transforms the world.

As you can see, mission statements range from very simple to more complex. Some companies include their target market and/or their ethical position.

your business, think back to this mission statement and ask yourself, "Will taking this action support the mission of my company?" Also use your mission to help you reach your target market. By speaking clearly and confidently about why you are doing the work you are doing, people will become interested in you and want to learn more.

SUCCESSFUL NETWORKING

Building your business is about building relationships. The more people you meet and know, the more likely you are to find prospective clients, or create the possibility of having clients referred to you. Understanding and practicing networking will help you grow your business and spread the word about who you are and what you do. The larger your network of friends, colleagues, contacts and acquaintances becomes, the better your chance of success. People like working with people they know. As you become increasingly recognizable as a Health Counselor, you create what we call VFT.

- **Visibility:** being seen.
- **Familiarity:** the more often you are in contact with people, the more they remember you and your services.
- **Trust:** being reliable, responsive and knowledgeable fosters this relationship.

Networking is a way to expand the circle of people you know in order to increase the buzz about your business. If 100 people know that you are a Health Counselor and they each tell one person who tells one person about you, your chances of getting a phone call are dramatically higher than if only 20 people know you are a Health Counselor. And if 1,000 people know about you, your phone will ring even more!

Talk about what you do to as many people as possible. There are many benefits to networking, such as:

- Becoming known in your community as an expert in health and nutrition.
- Getting new ideas from others on how to provide your services and how to build your business.
- Creating the opportunity to schedule more health histories.
- Building referral systems with other professionals.
- Adding people to your contact list for all of your communications, emails, newsletters and workshop announcements.
- Having fun by meeting other people and learning who they are and what they do.

WHERE TO NETWORK

You can network anywhere: on the train, at the gym, at a restaurant or in a more formal networking atmosphere where everyone is there for the same reason. Here are some places you might want to think about networking:

- **Networking groups:** There are specific groups that exist for the sole purpose of bringing people together to make contacts and help one another build their businesses. Some of these groups include Business Network International (BNI) (www.bni.com) and National Women Business Owners (www.nwboc.org).

- **Associations or organizations in your field:** Many groups already exist for people who are interested in health and nutrition. To find out where some of these might be in your neighborhood, you'll have to do a little research. You can ask around at gyms, yoga studios and schools, and read the paper to see if there are any groups already in place. These are a great place to share with other counselors and nutritionists, especially those with different target markets. Also, if you have another area of interest or hobby, attending meetings with those people and talking about your new work as a Health Counselor is a great idea because you will already have something in common with them.

- **Trade and professional groups that your target market attends:** Many professions have associations and groups to which they belong. For example, if you are interested in working with women business professionals, you could attend various networking events for those women in your area.

- **Trade and professional groups that your referral partners are likely to attend:** Referral partners are critical to growing your business, whether they are doctors, chiropractors, yoga teachers, hair stylists or personal trainers. They each belong to and attend events based on their professions. You can attend those events, get to know them, and let them get to know you.

- **Lectures, workshops and conferences:** There are conferences on every topic, from health and healing, sports and entertainment to arts and crafts, exercise and finances. Find out when these events happen, and attend them. You may even want to lead a workshop. You will get more information about workshops later in this chapter.

- **Social, cultural or sporting events, including mixers and parties:** You never know when you are going to meet a potential client or referral partner. When you start health counseling, it is helpful for you to be social and to connect with people who you haven't seen in awhile. You could get clients at your high school reunion, by meeting up with an old friend or meeting new people when you are out.

- **Charity events and fundraisers:** You may want to donate a health history, a cooking class or even a condensed version of your six-month program to a charity to help increase your visibility. When you attend the event, you can tell people that you donated your services, and that will start a conversation about what you do as a Health Counselor.

Notes:

Where do you think you could most successfully network your services?

....

....

....

....

....

....

Once you have identified the types of events you think will be most beneficial to attend for building your network, you'll want to contact the organizations that host them. Here are some ways to find specific organizations if you don't already know where they are located.

- **Chamber of Commerce:** Your local Chamber of Commerce hosts various events and workshops. Contact them, and find out their schedule.

- **Yellow pages.**

- **Newspapers and magazines:** Various events, social outings and group gatherings are advertised in the paper.

- **Online:** Most major groups publish their information online. Go to Google or Yahoo, type in a search and see what comes up.

- **Specialized publications that your target market reads:** Look for specialty publications on any topic, from pets to medicine to teen health. Find these publications, read the event listings and contact key people.

- **Ask other people who are knowledgeable:** Talk with successful friends, colleagues and coworkers about where they network and what they suggest. Get to know people who are successful in business and find out how they network.

CREATE A NETWORKING CALENDAR

What groups, associations or organizations have you researched? When are their events?

Group ....

Event Date ....

Event Time ....

Location ....

When You Will Go ....

Group ....

Event Date ....

Event Time ....

Location ....

When You Will Go ....

Group ....

Event Date ....

Event Time ....

Location ....

When You Will Go ....

Group ....

Event Date ....

Event Time ....

Location ....

When You Will Go ....

Notes:

HOW TO NETWORK SUCCESSFULLY:

- Do the research and find out what is happening in your area, with your target market and with your referral partners. Use the steps above and make a list of all the events and groups you can find.

- Contact the groups, associations and people you've researched. Get a copy of their calendar and ask questions about their events and members.

- Pick a couple of networking groups related to your niche market, hobbies and interests.

Use the networking calendar you created above and start to attend events. Try them on.

- Networking is like dating; you may not click with every group you attend, but you are gaining valuable experience in the process. Try different groups and see which one feels right.

Notes:

- Start your own group. A great way to network is to contact people you know who also have their own business and are looking to make contacts. You can meet once a month or so and have tea, breakfast or lunch. Get to know one another and share ideas on business building. Begin to refer to others in your group and ask them to refer theirs to you. Great people to include are doctors, lawyers, business people, acupuncturists, massage therapists, hair stylists and accountants.

WHEN ATTENDING A NETWORKING EVENT

- Start talking to people, especially those you are drawn to, or ask the event organizer to introduce you to a few people. The more people you meet and add to your contact list, the more likely your business will grow. Be passionate about what you do; people know when you are sincere. Use your elevator speech.

- Use a firm handshake, look people in the eye and make a good connection. Pin your nametag on your right side so it's more visible when you shake hands.

- Listen, be friendly and, show interest in others. Use the verbal skills you've learned in school on starting conversations and communicating effectively.

- At events, select a few "key" people to align yourself with. Organizers and promoters usually know most of the people, and they can be a great resource for you. You could even volunteer at an event and introduce yourself to all the attendants.

NETWORKING TIPS FOR INTROVERTED PEOPLE

- Take a small step outside your comfort zone. Even researching events is a great beginning.
- Be patient.
- Get support.
- Invite an extroverted friend with you to the event. They can introduce you to people and help you feel more at ease.
- Introduce yourself on the phone to the event leader, and go to tea with them as a first step before diving into the group.
- Volunteer. This is a perfect opportunity to help others and meet people.
- Use our tips for good conversation skills and ice-breakers for small talk.
- Speak to the people you feel most drawn to.
- Avoid large groups that are intimidating; instead speak to one or two people at a time.
- Start by asking others questions about what they do. Get them talking. Then, either they will ask what you do, or you can tell them.

- Always give people your business card and be sure to get everyone else's cards as well. Have an organized way to keep track of the business cards you collect as discussed in Chapter 1. Make notes on the back of the business cards about the people you meet so you remember what you talked about and how to follow up with them.

- Be gracious. Ask people you meet to put you on their mailing list. Show them you are interested in what they do.

- If you find yourself stuck in a conversation with someone, you can politely excuse yourself to get water or use the restroom. Always be considerate, but don't waste your valuable time with people who drain you.

Remember that your goal is to connect with people and build your contacts. It's always helpful to share what you do. Even more important is to listen, create a connection and be sure to get people's contact information. You may even offer to send them something they could find helpful (an article you wrote, a name of a great book) as it relates to the conversation you had with them. Your goal is not to hand out as many business cards as possible. It's about having conversations with people who may be interested in your work, and finding ways to stay in touch.

When you get home that night or the next day, record the contact information of the people you met. Keep track of them—remember VFT. Subscribe them to your newsletter if they've given you permission. You have to be proactive and take the initiative to contact others since they probably won't contact you, so send them a follow-up email. Try to attend at least two networking events per month. Networking and building a business take time, and it's okay to make mistakes. Just remember to keep moving forward!

APPROACHING PEOPLE

A big part of building a business is being able to meet new people and passionately share what you do. Whether at a networking event, on the street, at a party or at a meeting, socializing is a great way to build your contact list. Often times, though, we are afraid to approach other people. We worry whether we will know the right words to say, whether the person will like us, or whether the conversation will go well. People naturally have a need to connect, so it's important to find ways to be more comfortable reaching out. The following tips should help you with your ability to start making connections:

- Start with people you know; practice saying hello and articulating what you do. This will help you build your confidence so when you talk with strangers you'll feel more comfortable.

- If you are going to an event, make a list of talking points and conversation starters.

- Bring friends with you to events, so you feel more supported.

Notes:

NETWORKING MISTAKES

- Talking too much.
- Lack of eye contact.
- Asking for business, being pushy.
- Showing up in casual, sloppy clothes.
- Only hanging out with people you already know.
- Forgetting to offer or invite people to do anything.
- Going to the event hungry and eating the whole time.
- Focusing on getting clients rather than building relationships.

- Start talking with people whom you don't find as intimidating. You may not be comfortable telling the president of your company about your workshops, but you may feel fine talking with your colleague in the lunchroom. Start small, and keep practicing.
- Smile, try your best, and just start talking. Say hello to the clerk behind the counter, talk with the other parents at your child's school. Even if it's only a few sentences, practice.
- Remember, you have nothing to lose. Even if the conversation doesn't go as well as you want, everything is still ok. You can move on and talk with other people.

MAKING SMALL TALK

When you are out there approaching people, it's helpful to have some icebreakers to start the conversation. These phrases are subtle and non-intrusive ways to help you connect with a new person, and not feel any pressure. They will get you and the other person talking and might lead to a health history or a workshop connection. If not, at least you are building your communication confidence.

- Opening questions require more than just a simple yes or no answer. Example: At a health food store you can ask, "So what do you know about whole grains?"
- Make a simple comment to stimulate conversation. Example: "Those apples look very fresh. Do you buy them at the farmers' market often?"
- An occasion statement refers to something that is going on around you or the location. Example: "I've never been to this networking event before. Have you ever attended?"
- Give a compliment. Example: "I like your bag; where did you find that?"
- Ask for someone's opinion. Example: "I've never been to this health food store; what do you recommend?"

- Make a general comment. Example: "This workshop is one of the best I've been to."

WORKSHOPS

Leading workshops is one of the best ways to get clients. It is also a great opportunity for you to practice being in front of the room and to strengthen your communication skills. By teaching a group of people topics related to health and nutrition, you will really start to become an expert.

Your confidence will increase, and you will begin to acknowledge how much more you know about health than the average person.

In the beginning, aim for getting five to 10 people in a workshop. As you build your public speaking skills and expand your business, you can lead workshops for increasingly more people. The idea is to attract the types of people whom you want as clients. You can present at community centers, libraries, health food stores, women's groups, schools, universities, health centers, wellness centers, gyms and even your own home.

When you approach a new location about doing a workshop, it is always helpful to visit the location in person, introduce yourself and ask who is in charge of programs or scheduling. Once you are talking to this person, indicate that you are looking to volunteer to do workshops to help the organization. Give them your elevator speech and ask, "How can I help support you by bringing in more people to this location and offering my expertise to the community you serve?" Play the role of a Health Counselor. Make the workshop a win/win situation for both you and the location.

We suggest that you bring your press kit (learn more about how to create this kit in Chapter 6, "Your Program Offerings") with you when visiting potential workshop spaces. You can include an outline of your proposed workshop in the press kit, along with a page full of positive feedback you've collected from participants at past workshops (if you have this).

WORKSHOP MARKETING

You don't have a workshop unless you have participants. So marketing your workshop is essential. The following steps are ways to promote your workshop:

- Post flyers at key locations: health food stores, community centers, bookstores or any locations where your potential target market spends time.
- Tell everyone you know about the workshop: clients, friends, family and colleagues. Have them tell people and offer them a referral incentive. You could have them send out the invitation to their entire mailing list. An important point to keep in mind is to touch base with as many people as possible who are connected to your target market. Find those who already have a preexisting contact list of qualified candidates.

Notes:

- Send an email announcement to your contact list.

- Mention the workshop in your newsletter.

- Invite people from the organization where you are giving the workshop. Encourage them to post the event in their announcement board or newsletter so more people know about your talk.

- Go to other events and make yourself known. Hand out flyers at expositions, social gatherings, health fairs and similar events.

- Post on websites: yours or websites of any of your referral partners.

- Take out an ad in a publication that your target market reads.

- Place an announcement in the events listing section of local newspapers or newsletters.

- Post the workshop details on community or event websites that your target market may see, in the events section or upcoming listings.

It's a good idea to ask people to sign up for your workshop in advance so that you know who is coming. You can do this by having them RSVP to you or the location that is holding your workshop.

If you have people RSVP to the location, be sure to give the location a sign-up sheet that they can use to keep track of your participants, including names, telephone numbers and email addresses, as well as how they heard about your workshop (which is helpful for future marketing).

PRESENTING THE WORKSHOP

The workshop begins long before the actual start time. Familiarize yourself with the outline and handouts we provide for the Sugar Blues talk. If you are creating your own workshop topic, use that outline and format to design your own workshop. Or you can use the template provided below to create an agenda. Practice your talk on your own at home or for friends. Find an assistant, someone to come with you as your support person. The day before your workshop, send a reminder email out to participants. It is also important that you exercise, eat well, center yourself and arrive 30 minutes early. Then make sure you have everything you need, including:

- Workshop outline: You may want to print this out in a large font size so that it is easy for you to read.

- Your assistant to provide support, pass out handouts and help schedule participants for health history consultations.

- Your business cards.

- A sign-in sheet for health history consultations with actual time/day slots that you are available. Prepare this before the workshop by referencing your calendar to find times when you can do the sessions.

- Handouts related to your talk.

- Snacks/food to give out (fruit, trail mix, simple treats).

- A watch in case there is not a working clock at the location.

TIPS FOR CONDUCTING THE WORKSHOP

- Greet guests warmly.

- Have everyone fill out the sign-in sheet. Your support person can help.

- Start strong, and share information about yourself so attendees can relate to you. Share why you do this work or something about your own journey. You may want to share how you came to be interested in nutrition. All this helps you be real to your audience.

- Follow your outline. It's okay to go on a short tangent or to incorporate ideas not on the outline, but use the outline to guide you and keep you focused.

- Use humor when appropriate; it helps people feel comfortable.

- Bring props, something to catch the participants' attention. It could be an ad for unhealthy food from a magazine or a box of sugar. Pick something that feels right to you.

- Don't give all of your information away. Talk more about what's "wrong" than about tips on what to do. If you say too much, attendees will not be as inclined to want to work with you.

- For example, talk about the health consequences of eating too much sugar, not necessarily how to stop eating sugar.

- Be interactive. Use paired shares, group shares and call on people.

- Have giveaways and handouts that participants can take with them.

- Connect participants to the concept of how difficult it is to be unhealthy. Call on one volunteer; ask them to share the pain of being unhealthy and how it has affected their life and health. By doing so, you make that person and all participants more aware of their current situation, and they in turn may realize that they need guidance to feel better.

- Share examples of client successes at appropriate times.

- Stop for stretch breaks and for questions.

- Share goals. Ask participants what they would like to make happen in their lives. Have them share this verbally or write.

WRAPPING UP THE WORKSHOP

- Do a paired share and have participants talk about what they learned at the workshop—one thing they will take with them.

- Leave enough time to talk about your program, explaining what you do while sharing the value of working with a Health Counselor.

- Use a call-to-action technique. Remind participants that real change comes from taking action; so now it's time to move towards the goals they mentioned in the workshop. That comes by first signing up for a free health history. Also, tell them if they go home and think about it or don't sign up in the moment, it's more likely they will just stay stuck. You are offering a free hour of your time to discuss their goals more deeply, and explore how you would support them in your six-month program to create a truly amazing life.

- Have your assistant sign people up for health history consultations, using the sign-up sheet you created. Write the date and time of each consultation on the back of your business card, and hand these to health history clients.

- Give your card to all workshop participants. Thank them for their active participation.

FOLLOW UP

- Send thank-you emails to participants; thank them for their time.

- Add everyone's contact information to your mailing list.

- Send a confirmation email to health history clients to remind them of their session time.

- Send some type of email handout related to the content of your workshop to each participant. When you give something extra after the workshop, participants see you as a valuable and knowledgeable support person.

TOP 10 WAYS TO GET CLIENTS FROM YOUR LECTURES:

1. **Bring food:** Nothing attracts participants to your workshop like free food. This is a way for them to taste the types of foods they could expect to learn how to make and also gives them something tangible to grasp.

2. **Tell client success stories:** Try to sprinkle your talk with several stories of success. For example, "When one of my clients, a busy mother of three, came to me, she was totally hooked on sugar. These days, after adding some of the tools I suggested, she is much more energized without the need for sweets." Clarify what the problem was before and how you helped that person. This presents you as a problem solver and gives you credibility. If you don't have one to talk about,

think about the health concerns you've overcome or the people you've helped over the years.

3. **Make your talk interactive:** Don't talk at them, talk with them. Encourage interactive elements such as paired shares, group shares and group exercises. People love to talk. They are much more likely to be interested in your talk if you include them.

4. **Do a mini-counseling session demo in front of the class:** Not only does this establish your credibility and expertise, it gives the participants an idea of how you work and your style of counseling. If they like what they see and the results you have with your counseling demo, they will be more likely to sign up with you.

5. **Collect useful contact information:** Be sure to have participants sign in and share their email and mailing address. This is a great opportunity to invite them to receive your email newsletter. Even if they don't sign up for a consultation, you can add them to your newsletter and they will remain on your radar. When they think of nutrition and wellness, they will think of you.

6. **Provide a valuable giveaway:** You want them to go home with a useful tip that they can refer to often, with your contact name on it. You can give away a favorite recipe that's related to your talk, tip sheet, special report or article. Perhaps they will pass it on to someone who is interested, or simply think of you when they use it.

7. **Bring an assistant:** This can be a classmate, a buddy or someone who loves and supports you. Let them handle the logistics of signing people in, collecting contact info and scheduling health histories for you. If you need anything, they can support you. This will give you time to mingle and interact with participants, and it also makes you look very professional. Alternatively, you can bring a client who's willing to share the benefits of working with you as a testimonial.

8. **Make sure the audience knows what you do:** Many times people do not sign up for a consultation because they have never been asked. Leave time in your talk to introduce your services. Remind yourself that what you offer is an opportunity. Otherwise, it's just another lecture full of tips that they will never use. The best way you can help them is to offer them your program. You also want to leave time at the end of your talk to mingle and answer questions.

9. **Circulate an evaluation form:** Sometimes people are shy or just need to think about things. A great way to get feedback on your talk is to create an evaluation form. Ask what they liked, learned and enjoyed. Ask what future topics they would like to hear about. Most importantly, ask if they would like to learn more about one-on-one health counseling and when would be a good time to call. Be sure to include space for a phone number and email address. We provide you with a sample evaluation form.

10. **Make sure attendees have a way of contacting you after the lecture.** Put a brochure or business card on each person's chair. It gives them something to read when they arrive and helps them be clear on who is giving the talk. Get used to giving your materials out like hotcakes.

OVERCOMING NERVOUSNESS

You might be nervous about giving a workshop. That's totally normal. In fact, public speaking is often the biggest fear our students face. It's one of those times where you'll have to feel the fear and do it anyway. By the end of the year, most of our students become comfortable and confident public speakers, and it is one of their favorite aspects of this work. Here are some helpful tips on overcoming the fear of public speaking:

Prepare: The more you prepare, the more comfortable you will be with your workshop. Plan ahead what you want to talk about by making an outline. Consider what objectives you want to have for your workshop. What do you want your audience to get out of it? For example, you may want them to leave your workshop with an ability to identify hidden sugars in foods. You almost always will want them to sign up for a health history consultation with you. Once you know your objectives, you can create an agenda to meet those objectives. Your agenda becomes a roadmap. When you create your agenda, think about how much time you will allot to each topic you will cover, as well as how you will conduct that part of the workshop (e.g., a lecture versus a paired share or group activity) and any materials or handouts you will need.

Below is an outline template that you can use to create a workshop agenda:

WORKSHOP OBJECTIVE

What you will cover	How	Timing	Materials needed

Breathe: One of the best things you can do to stay grounded and focused when leading a workshop is to breathe. Use the paired shares and group shares as a time for you to check in with yourself and make sure you are breathing and relaxed.

Start small: If you are very nervous about leading a workshop, you may want to start small. You can invite three or four friends over for a workshop in your home. You can practice with them and ask them for feedback, what you did well and what you could improve. Realize that everyone wants you to be successful. Anyone who comes to your workshop is there because they want to learn from you and have a positive experience. They are on your side and want the workshop to go well just as much as you do. Understanding this and believing it, will go a long way towards helping you relax into your role as the workshop facilitator.

NEWSLETTER

Your newsletter is a fundamental part of your health counseling business. Each time you meet someone, you should ask them if they would like to be on your newsletter list. Be sure to get people's business cards. This way, as you add more and more people to your list over time, you are increasing your prospects. Again, the more you reach out to people, the more likely they are to remember you and want to work with you. It is a relatively simple way for you to get information out to a lot of people at one time. It can be part of the "Free Stuff" section of your website, or a free giveaway that you offer during networking and as part of your six-month program. Also, writing your newsletter is an educational and creative outlet for you. To write a good newsletter, you'll have to pick a topic interesting to you and do a little research. Then you get to let your personality come out and write it in a way that expresses who you are. To help you with this, we will provide you with several newsletters to get you started. You can use these newsletters just as they are, tweak them to make them more "yours" or write your own, using them as idea generators.

DIFFERENT WAYS TO SEND OUT YOUR NEWSLETTER:

- **Snail Mail:** While this is an option, we do not recommend it because of the high costs involved (printing, mailing) and the trouble of addressing the envelopes.
- **Email:** You can simply copy your newsletter into the body of an email and create an email distribution list. This option is okay at first if you only have a few people to send your newsletter to, but you will quickly grow out of this.
- **Yahoo Group:** Some Health Counselors choose to send their newsletters out via a Yahoo chat group. The advantage of this method is that people can sign up for your newsletter via Yahoo, and you do not need to personally manage the distribution list as you would if you were just sending out an email.

Notes:

- **Online Newsletter Service:** This is the best and most professional option. There are several online newsletter services that you can use to send out your newsletter. Webvalence (www.webvalence.com) and Constant Contact (www.constantcontact.com) are two examples. These services cost about $30 per month. They have templates that are easy to use, or you can design your own. You simply copy or type your newsletter into their website and schedule it to be sent at a certain time. Once it goes out, you can track who read your newsletter, when they read it and what links they clicked on (if any). If you have a website, you can add an email newsletter sign-up box to it so that visitors can easily register to receive your newsletter.

TELECLASSES

If many of your clients are phone clients, you may want to offer your monthly seminars as teleclasses. You can schedule an hour-long teleclass each month. Topics can range from cooking tips to Sugar Blues to Eating for Energy. Almost anything that can be taught in person can also be taught on the phone. Record your call and make it available for people to listen to afterwards.

Even if your clients are local and you hold in-person seminars, teleclasses are a low-cost, convenient way to expand your business and spread the word about your company. There are many free or low-cost companies you can use to set up a teleclass. You may schedule your teleclass on www.freeconference.com or www.nocostconference.com. They each have recording services to keep your call.

We recommend doing teleclasses for free at first while getting a sense of what does and doesn't work. Once you feel comfortable, you may charge. Typical fees are anywhere from $19 to $29 per class. You will need to be set up to accept credit cards in order to receive payments for teleclasses. You can use www.paypal.com or www.oneshoppingcart.com to collect fees.

REASONS TO LEAD A TELECLASS:

- Access to potential clients from the comfort of your home, with no travel time required.
- All you need is a phone and a headset.
- Access to people who can refer you to potential clients.
- You build credibility with potential clients.
- Deepening of relationships with existing clients.
- Reduced marketing budget (no costs for space or materials).
- Get known for being an expert.
- Talk with people who want to hear what you have to say.
- Get more participation since shy people can speak up.
- An opportunity to test new material and ideas.

WAYS TO PROMOTE YOUR TELECLASS:

- Send an invitation to every contact on your mailing list.
- Mention your upcoming teleclass to in-person participants at your workshops.
- Promote in your newsletter: list the topic description and how to register for the class.
- Have referral partners and colleagues mention the teleclass to their contact groups and/or list the class in their newsletter.
- Promote your class on websites that your target market visits.
- Place a classified listing (free or low-cost) in a periodical that your target market frequently reads.
- Please remember to begin your marketing at least three to four weeks before the actual date, to make sure you have as many callers as possible.
- In your promotions, be sure to mention the benefits of the class, and what the participants will get out of it. Also tell them how to register for the class (email or link on your website), and give them a deadline to do so.

HOW TO DEVELOP A TELECLASS:

- Brainstorm topics and decide on the content you want to deliver.
- Design your outline and stages of your talk.
- Decide whom you'd like to invite to your teleclass.
- Determine how you will market the teleclass.
- Pick a day and time.
- Schedule the class.
- Decide whether you'd like to charge for the class (we recommend doing them free at first, to build your contacts and experience).
- Set up the conference call line.
- Invite participants (include day and time of talk, plus class description).
- Send call-in number and access code to enrolled participants. They can enroll by sending you an email confirming their interest (if charging, send them the financial processing service's link and wait until their payment has been processed).
- Send out reminders one or two days before the talk.
- Practice your talk beforehand.
- You can use a professional service to record your teleclass, so the participant can listen again after, or those who were not available at that date and time can attend. You may even decide to offer a link to your class recording on your website.

STAGES OF A TELECLASS CURRICULUM:

- Introduction: warmly welcome everyone to your talk.
- Share your excitement and a personal story about you, and relate that story to your talk.
- Tell them what to expect from the call, reviewing outline bullet points.
- Remind them of the class protocol: pay attention, mute phone when not speaking, put other stuff down.
- Start your talk, following the outline you created.
- Do a group share in the middle of the talk to check in around topic content or to see if there are questions.
- Summarize what you talked about in the call.
- Thank them for their attention.
- Allow a Q&A session, depending on the time remaining.
- Offer an invitation to a health history. Tell the participants that you are offering this as a special bonus to the teleclass participants. If they would like to set up a time, tell them they can do so by calling you or by emailing you. You can also say that you will send everyone an email after the call to clarify what the health history is and how to schedule one.
- You can also use your teleclass to promote any other services, including a group program or other items unique to your practice.
- Send them a special handout, article or other gift after the class.
- Follow up with the email health history invitation, including your website, contact information, and a client testimonial or case study.
- Respond to those who write you.

MARKETING MATERIALS

When you go out and meet potential clients, you'll want to have marketing materials that convey who you are and what you do. We will provide you with business cards, brochures and a website to get you started. While you are a student, we want you to focus on marketing yourself, building business relationships and doing health histories, not spending your precious time and money at your computer designing marketing materials, as you are your best marketing tool.

As your business grows, you may eventually create your own logo, color scheme and style for your marketing materials. The look and feel of these materials should be consistent with how you want people to experience your services. For example, if you work primarily with women, you may want your marketing materials to feature lighter colors and more feminine images. If you work with male athletes, you may want your materials to have a stronger, more masculine quality.

To get a high-quality logo, you can hire a graphic designer. A good graphic designer will work with you to understand what you want the image of your business to represent. Through this process, the designer will show you some options for logos. He or she may also help you pick out colors and fonts for your business and design your business card. Before hiring a designer and agreeing to the fee, you should be very clear on what exactly you are paying for. How many drafts of your logo do you want? Usually, this kind of work demands three drafts: the first draft illustrates brainstorming about the look, feel and colors; the second draft shows the direction you have chosen; and the final draft is tweaked to get it exactly as you like it. It can cost $300 to $1,500 for the design of a logo. If you know a skilled graphic designer you could barter with, that may be a good option. Alternatively, you can use an online service, such as Vistaprint.com, that has a selection of logos. You can pick one that works for you and create your own business cards, brochures, notepads, postcards and more. Using such a service, you can also upload your own original logo onto these materials and print them out. Please keep in mind, this is not required when you start out. What's most important is developing a consistent marketing plan.

MARKETING MATERIALS:

- **Business Cards:** Your business card will represent you long after you have given it away. The front of your card should include your name, title (e.g., Health Counselor), company name, telephone number, email address, website address and logo. You can also include your physical office address and fax number. The back of the card can be used as well. Here you can have a cool design, an inspirational quote, a tagline or a listing of your services.

- **Brochures:** A brochure is great to take with you to networking meetings or give out at talks. Your brochure should match your business card in look and feel and can include parts of your core mission: whom you work with, the concerns they have, the benefits they get from working with you and what makes your services unique. You should include your name, title, company name, address, phone number, email address and website address. You may also want to include a short section that describes who you are, including your educational background and training. We will give you a predesigned brochure. In addition, a company such as VistaPrint can help you create your brochure, or you can create your own using software such as Microsoft Word or PowerPoint.

- **Your Bio:** Your biography is a few sentences of background information on who you are and what you do. You may have a couple of versions of your bio that you can use in different circumstances. It should include pieces of your mission, such as whom you work with and how you help them. You can also include your educational background and any special trainings or certifications. We discuss bios more in chapter 7, "Marketing and Business Development Strategies."

- **Website:** You will be provided a website from the school. Your website (either from the school or one you develop yourself) will expand on your core mission even more than your brochure does. It should match your other marketing materials in terms of the look and feel. Pages to have on your website might be: "Home," "Who we work with," "How we help," "Services," "About us," "Success stories" and "Free stuff." The Free stuff page can offer any articles you've written, recipes or back issues of your newsletter. This page is a great marketing tool—a way to get people to linger on your site a little longer than they might have otherwise. There are many online website host companies that provide templates for new websites. As mentioned in Chapter 3, we recommend Start Logic or Go Daddy. Please be sure to share your website with everyone you know, and have this be a place for potential clients to learn more about you and your work, which helps them understand how your services will be of benefit to them.

HEALTH FAIRS

Many Health Counselors use health fairs as a way to increase their visibility in the community. It can be a public health fair or a private fair for a business or an organization. You can find out about health fairs by talking to other health practitioners or by signing up with a health fair organizer. Most of these organizers are local, so ask around to find one in your area.

At the fair, you will most likely have a table or booth to display your business. Here are some things you might want to bring with you to the fair:

- Brochures
- Business cards
- Sign-up sheet for your newsletter
- Tablecloth (unless one is provided for you)
- Large sign with your business name on it
- Sign-up sheet for free health history consultations
- Some kind of free giveaway: food samples, tea, organic chocolate
- Bouquet of pretty flowers in a vase to draw attention to your table
- Some kind of raffle opportunity: people fill out a small questionnaire with their name and contact information and get entered into a drawing for a free month of health counseling, a book, a basket of healthy goodies, etc.

DRESS TO IMPRESS

The importance of maintaining a professional image cannot be emphasized enough. How you present yourself to the world sends a message about how you view yourself. One way to send out a message that you are professional is to dress that way. This does not mean that you need to wear a business suit every day. It means that you ought to dress in a way that makes you feel good about yourself and reflects your work as a Health Counselor. If your target market is yoga teachers, wearing a business suit to a workshop is inappropriate. Likewise, if your target market is corporate professionals, wearing flip-flops and jeans is not the best first impression. You want to dress in a way that people in your target will be drawn to you, relate to you and also see you as competent. You also want to be comfortable and confident in your clothing.

Keep in mind that you never really know where your next client might be. You could meet him or her in the grocery store, at Starbuck's, at a restaurant or on the train. For this reason, consider dressing to impress every time you leave the house.

GRADUATE PROFILE

MAYA BHAGAT
Bloomfield, NJ
WellBeingPrana@aol.com
2006 Graduate

> " ...get out of (your) own way, take control... schedule and prioritize (your) work more effectively... "

I work full-time leading a global logistics team in export transportation. A year ago, I was operating on autopilot, going into the office early and staying late every day. I would visit doughnut shops and the vending machines daily, and grab dinner at any place that was still open at 10 p.m. My weekends were spent recovering, preparing for another week of the same. A major health problem created a turning point in my life and an opportunity to take an honest look at myself.

Integrative Nutrition appeared at exactly the right time. During the school year, I took control of my health and stress level, while creating a part-time business that sings to my soul. With the skills and confidence I gained at the school, I was able to establish healthy boundaries at my job. I was able to get out of my own way, take control of my schedule and prioritize my work more effectively so I am not burning myself out.

I got my practice started by doing health histories and Sugar Blues talks over and over again. My first talk was at a holistic health center, with an audience of five or six people. They didn't seem to pick up on my fears, and one person signed up immediately for the program. From there, I booked talks at Whole Foods, the YMCA and the Girl Scouts. I kept doing talks, breaking through my fears around public speaking and becoming more comfortable each time. News of my business spread through these speaking engagements, and I continued getting health histories and new clients. By the time I graduated, I had 11 paying clients.

Through my experience with doing talks, I've learned that it's just as easy and much more effective to book a series of talks rather than one at a time. This way I am doing less marketing and saving time. I do monthly talks at the YMCA on various health topics, and I recently completed a three-part lecture series for the Girl Scouts, with more planned for the future.

A beautiful thing I learned at the school is that when someone doesn't sign up for my program or book a talk, it doesn't mean I'm a bad person or that I'm not good enough. I ask myself what I can try differently next time instead of staying paralyzed in rejection or defeat. It's much more empowering to see these situations as opportunities to learn and grow.

I was amazed by how much business information the school provided. They present a banquet of choices, where you can pick and choose what tips and techniques to use. The tips are simple, specific and strategic. The school has really figured out how you can get the most results from your effort, so trust the process and take action.

I have come so far in such a short period of time. It's astounding what you can accomplish during the school year, so jump in and use all the resources and support to make an amazing career and life for yourself.

Notes:

....
....
....
....
....
....
....
....
....
....
....
....
....
....
....
....
....
....
....
....
....
....
....
....
....
....
....

If you hear a voice within you say 'you cannot paint,' then by all means paint, and that voice will be silenced.

—Vincent Van Gogh

CHAPTER 5:

SUCCESSFULLY SIGNING ON CLIENTS

Typically, people attracted to health counseling are intelligent, unique, intuitive and generous. It is very common for them to have difficulty asking for money. If you want to be successful as a Health Counselor, you will have to overcome blocks around money and your value. We will support you in this process throughout the year, but the best way for you to learn is to simply practice closing the deal. Closing the deal is the part at the end of a health history where you ask your potential client if they want to work with you. For some people it comes easily, but for most people it is the most difficult part of the health history. In this chapter, we will walk you through the different aspects of closing the deal and provide you with information and tools on how to do this successfully.

ENDING THE HEALTH HISTORY

After you go through the Health History Form, leave about 10 to 15 minutes to close the deal. As we mentioned in Chapter 2, here are some steps to take:

- Mention one thing you enjoyed about your potential client and the session.
- Ask them, "How was this for you?"
- Ask them, "What was one thing you found valuable in our session?"
- Restate some of the person's health concerns and the three things they know they could be doing for their health that they are not doing.
- Explain in detail what they get from your six-month program. (You may want to get out your Program Agreement, which clearly lists everything that is included in your program. Sometimes having a visual of all this information is helpful.)

- Two one-hour appointments each month for six months, which will include discussion of the client's progress, recommendations and a full set of notes.

- A variety of handouts, recipes, books, CDs, foods and other materials.

- Monthly special events like a health food store tour and group discussions related to health and wellness (the health food store tour is optional for you to include, you may want to just give or loan them a copy of the DVD from the school).

- An invitation to bring guests to the special events.

- Email support in between sessions.

- Let them know that all of this is included in your monthly fee.
- Ask them, "How does all of this sound to you?" or "How do you see this program being a benefit to help you to reach your goals?"
- Ask, "Do you have any questions?" They will probably ask how you accept payments. Explain that they can either pay in-full or in monthly installments. Explain that they can pay via cash, check or credit card (if you take credit cards).

EXAMPLE OF SPECIFIC LANGUAGE FOR EXPLAINING PROGRAM COST

"The program is $95 per month, and that includes everything: our meetings, recommendations, handouts, helpful books and CDs, my newsletter, and email support in between sessions."

POWER STATEMENTS

The following statements are useful tools for you to close the deal successfully, wrapping up health histories in a way that will make potential clients more likely to sign up. Use these as you like and feel free to adapt them to your style:

- During the six months that we'll be working together, I am committed to teaching you a set of skills you will be able to use for the rest of your life.

- I will offer you recommendations that are enjoyable, easily integrated, and step-by-step, to work towards your goals.

- When we begin to work together, I think a perfect place to start would be (mention three things identified in the health history).

- We would work together for the next six months, which gives us time to get to know each other and to make slow but lasting changes.

- I could give you a list of 25 things to do and you would probably do them for a week—and then the list would go under the bed with the dust bunnies.

- We would check in with what is going on with you and see how the recommendations went from our last session.

- You would always leave with a list of recommendations to put into action in the two weeks between our sessions.

- Much of the program is driven by you, and no two programs are the same. Each one is completely individualized, based on your goals, your needs and the pace at which you want to go.

- In addition to our 12 sessions, I support you with books, materials, recipes, food samples and handouts that enhance the changes you are making.

POWER QUESTIONS

These questions are very helpful in closing the deal and having the potential client focused on how to make the program work:

- What are your top three goals?
- How will you feel once you've reached these goals?
- How would you like my support to reach these goals?
- When do you think we could start working together?

BONUS

For those of you who are really comfortable with asking the questions above, you can ask a bonus question: "Do you know anyone who might be interested in doing a health history with me?" If they say yes, get that person's name and find out the best way to contact them.

THE PROGRAM AGREEMENT

This Program Agreement is a document that you will give people once they say they want to sign up for your program. It is important to have every client sign this form. It contains your program offerings, price, disclaimer and a legal waiver. We will provide you with a copy of this form.

PROGRAM AGREEMENT

It is a pleasure to welcome you to this Program. During the upcoming six months, you will learn ways to help yourself achieve a healthier lifestyle. Please read the following. If anything is unclear, please ask.

This Agreement is made today between the Counselor of the Program and the person named at the end of this document, [the Client]. The Program in which you are about to enroll will include all of the following:

A. Two one-hour appointments each month for six months, which will include discussion of your progress, recommendations and a full set of notes.

B. Monthly, special events like a health food store tour or teleclasses related to health and wellness.

C. An invitation for guests to attend special events.

D. A variety of handouts, recipes, books, tapes, foods and other materials.

SCHEDULING

I understand that my clients have busy schedules and I take pride in not keeping them waiting or keeping them longer than planned. Each session will end an hour after it was scheduled to begin. Please be on time. If the Client needs to cancel or reschedule the appointment, the Client must do so 24 hours in advance; otherwise, the Client will forfeit that appointment and not have an opportunity to reschedule it.

Program begins............................and ends...("End Date")

This program expires if all 12 sessions have not been completed within two months after the End Date specified above.

PAYMENTS AND REFUNDS

The Client understands that the regular cost of the Program is $195 per month for six months. However, registration today reduces that cost to $150 per month. Upon commencement of the Program, the full amount of $900 is due and must be paid in full. However, in order to help the Client afford this Program, the Client may pay Program Fee in monthly installments by credit card or a series of post-dated checks. If the Client selects to pay in full, then the cost shall be reduced by another $100 (for a total cost of $800).

In the event of the Client's absence or withdrawal, for any reason whatsoever, the Client will remain fully responsible for the unpaid balance of the Program. Under no circumstance will the Counselor refund any payments made by the Client. By signing this Agreement, the Client agrees to be legally obligated to pay the full amount of this Program.

DISCLAIMER OF HEALTHCARE RELATED SERVICES

The Counselor encourages the Client to continue to visit and to be treated by his/her healthcare professionals, including, without limitation, a physician. The Client understands that the Counselor is not acting in the capacity of a doctor, licensed dietitian-nutritionist, massage therapist, psychologist or other licensed or registered professional. Accordingly, the client understands that the Counselor is not providing healthcare, medical or nutrition therapy services and will not diagnose, treat or cure in any manner whatsoever any disease, condition or other physical or mental ailment of the human body.

The Client has chosen to work with the Counselor and understands that the information received should not be seen as medical or nursing advice and is certainly not meant to take the place of your seeing licensed health professionals.

PERSONAL RESPONSIBILITY AND RELEASE OF HEALTHCARE RELATED CLAIMS

The Client acknowledges that the Client takes full responsibility for the Client's life and well-being, as well as the lives and well-being of the Client's family and children (where applicable), and all decisions made during and after this program.

The Client expressly assumes the risks of the Program, whether or not such risks were created or exacerbated by the Counselor. The Client releases the Counselor, his/her heirs, executors, administrators and assigns, its officers, directors, shareholders, employees, teachers, lecturers, agents, health counselors and staff (collectively, the Releasees) from any and all liability, damages, causes of action, allegations, suits, sums of money, claims and demands whatsoever, in law, admiralty or equity, which against the Releasees, the Client ever had, now has or will have in the future against the Releasees, arising from the Client's past or future participation in, or otherwise with respect to, the Program, unless arising from the gross negligence of the Releasees.

CHOICE OF LAW, ARBITRATION AND LIMITED REMEDIES

This agreement shall be construed according to the laws of the State of [your state]. In the event that any provision of this Agreement is deemed unenforceable, the remaining portions of the Agreement shall be severed and remain in full force. In the event a dispute arises between the parties, either arising from this Agreement or otherwise pertaining to the relationship between the parties, the parties will submit to binding arbitration before the American Arbitration Association (Commercial Arbitration and Mediation Center for the Americas Mediation and Arbitration Rules). Any judgment on the award rendered by the arbitrator(s) may be entered in any court having jurisdiction thereof. Such arbitration shall be conducted by a single arbitrator. The sole remedy that can be awarded to the Client in the event that an award is granted in arbitration is refund of the Program Fee. Without limiting the generality of the foregoing, no award of consequential or other damages, unless specifically set forth herein, may be granted to the Client.

If the terms of this Agreement are acceptable, please sign the acceptance below. By doing so, the Client acknowledges that: (1)he/she has received a copy of this letter agreement; (2)he/she has had an opportunity to discuss the contents with the Counselor and, if desired, to have it reviewed by an attorney; and (3) the Client understands, accepts and agrees to abide by the terms hereof.

Counselor name......................Signature...................................Date.........................

Client name ....Signature.................................Date.........................

As soon as people agree to sign up for your program, hand them this form and give them a moment to read it. We recommend that you state out loud your cancellation and refund policies, as well as the disclaimer that you are not a doctor. You want to be certain that your client understands these important details.

You must have all your clients sign this Program Agreement. Without it, there is no contract between you and your client, meaning your client could back out of the program at any time. Being clear about the Program Agreement is in the best interest of you and your client. Some clients will want a copy for their records, so bring two copies to each health history.

SCHEDULING CLIENTS

As soon as your client signs up for your six-month program and you both sign the Program Agreement, pick the days and times that you will have your sessions. Scheduling all your future sessions at the end of the first health history will reduce the amount of back and forth you have with the client throughout their program. Use the Program Schedule provided to help you organize these dates. Fill out this form with your clients after they sign the Program Agreement, and give them a copy or tell them you will give them a copy at their first session. Be sure to reiterate what it says on the bottom of the Program Schedule, which is that the sessions last one hour from the scheduled start time. If clients show up late, their sessions still end on time. Also stress the importance of your 24-hour cancellation policy. Once they sign up, send them a reminder email with the start date, time and location of their first session. In this email also thank them for agreeing to participate in your program, and remind them of the benefits they can expect.

PRICING YOUR PROGRAM

When pricing your program, start out with a cost that feels comfortable to you, but also compensates you fairly for your time and expertise. Inevitably, pricing your program is going to bring up issues you have around money. Please use your counselor and the OEF to get support.

Our students all come from different backgrounds. Some of them are new to having their own business, so the idea of making $50 per hour is very exciting. Other students come from professional backgrounds, where they are used to making over $100,000 a year. It's important for you to acknowledge where you are on this spectrum and be gentle with yourself along the way.

We recommend students start at around $75 to $95 per month. Some of you may already be used to charging this much. Maybe you are a massage therapist, nutritionist, physician or private yoga instructor. If this is the case, you can charge $150 or more for your first few clients. If charging $150 a month is scary for you, then you have two options: feel the fear and do it anyway or lower this fee. Perhaps you want to charge your first client $50 per month. If you do this, we encourage you to charge your second client $100 per month and so on.

You can raise your rates to $150, $195 or even $250 after graduation. Many graduates then raise their rates to $300 or $350 after another six months or a year of health counseling. Some go on to charge $450 or even $500 per month.

People can afford these prices. It's up to you to ask for them or not. When setting your fees, consider how many clients you actually want to work with and how much money you want to make from health counseling this year. See the "Business Plan" exercise in Chapter 7 to help you with this.

PROGRAM SCHEDULE

Client name: _____

Appointment day: _____

Appointment time: _____

	Individual sessions	Group events
Month 1	_____ _____	_____
Month 2	_____ _____	_____
Month 3	_____ _____	_____
Month 4	_____ _____	_____
Month 5	_____ _____	_____
Month 6	_____ _____	_____

Additional notes:

_____

_____

_____

_____

_____

_____

I understand that you have a busy schedule, and I pride myself on not keeping you waiting and not keeping you longer than planned. Your session will end an hour after it was scheduled to begin.

Please arrive on time. If you have a need to cancel your session, please do so at least 24 hours in advance.

LOWER-INCOME CLIENTS

If you want to offer your services to people who do not make a lot of money—such as young people, senior citizens or single parents—you have a few options:

Offer a Sliding Scale

When potential clients ask how much your program costs, you can say something along the lines of, "I have a sliding scale from $75 to $150 per month. What works for you?" Whether these are your actual parameters or you create others, you should still feel you are getting paid fairly for your services.

Group Programs

Another possibility is to offer group programs. You can then charge less per person while still making the same amount of money for your time. We will discuss group programs more thoroughly in Chapter 6, "Your Program Offerings."

Grant Funding

Applying for grants may work for you, especially if you want to work in schools or within certain communities.

DISCOUNTS

People love to save money. So if you want to charge $95 per month for your program, an effective sales strategy may be to tell potential clients that your program costs $150 per month, but if they sign up today (the day of the health history), you will give them a discount so that the program is $95 per month. You may also extend to them a reason why you are giving this discount. Perhaps it is because they are a young person or a single parent, or because you really want to work with them.

ASKING FOR MONEY

If this chapter about money makes you anxious, know that you will survive. You can still become a successful business owner, even if right now you are nervous about asking for money. Here are some strategies to help you overcome your concerns and confidently ask for the money you deserve:

1. Start your practice by taking on one or two barter clients so that you become confident in the value and effectiveness of your services. Then when you start asking for money, you will be very clear about what your clients are paying for. See more on bartering below.

2. Work on clearing up your money issues in your personal life. If you have difficulty asking for money in a business setting, this issue is probably coming up in all areas of your life. Are there a lot of people who owe you money? Do you

owe money? Do you have difficulty asking for what you want? Are you afraid of money? Do you feel that you don't deserve money? Practice asking people for money they owe you. Nurture and value the money you have. Get in the habit of happily receiving compliments, favors, gifts and money from others.

3. When closing the deal, focus on the other person, not on yourself. Learn that receiving money from your client benefits them by making it much more likely that they will reach their health goals. When you ask a potential client for money, the conversation is not about how much they value you, but about how much they value themselves. Asking your client for money is asking them to make a commitment to their own health. Paying you is an important action, symbolizing their investment in their well-being.

4. When you ask for money, all kinds of feelings may come up. Relax, stay focused and keep listening to the person. Your role is to show them everything they will get for their money and point out all the great benefits, and then support them to invest in themselves. You can point out that it is unfortunate that people spend so much money on clothes, cars, houses and going out to eat, but not on their bodies, which will be with them forever. You can support them to turn that around in their own lives.

5. Learn that payment for your work helps you have a positive relationship with your client. Money is energy. In order for you and your client to build a healthy, working relationship, the energy flow between you should be equal. You will be giving this person a great deal of your time and energy, not only in sessions, but also when you photocopy handouts, buy gifts, teach a cooking class, etc. You can view money as the way that they send energy back to you—creating a give-and-take relationship—so you both feel energized.

6. Know that an exchange of money for your services also helps keep clear boundaries between you and your clients. As a Health Counselor you will be warm, friendly and loving, but you are also a paid professional. It's important to keep this boundary clear, especially when it comes to the occasional client who misuses your time, bounces checks or treats you like a parent or best friend. Having clear, written agreements, and the appropriate exchange of money helps you set limits, keeping the counseling experience positive and happy for you.

ASKING FOR MONEY TIPS:

- Feel your fear, and do it anyway. Don't give into your fear about asking for money, because it will make your business stagnant.
- Practice your closing the deal statement with your buddy, friends and family. Asking for money is simply a muscle that needs flexing.
- Write down all the things that could happen when you ask for money: the person could say no, they could give you the money but resent you. If it's a

friend, it could hurt the friendship, etc. Write down all of your fears to get them out of your hair.

- Always be honest. Don't answer questions that you don't know the answer to, and don't promise anything that you can't deliver.
- Make sure potential clients know what they are getting for their money. Go over the Program Agreement Form and/or show them your rate sheet so they are clear.
- Tell a success story to illustrate what is possible if they work with you.

CASE STUDY

Here's an example of one student who wasn't appreciating her true value. Christina was charging $25 per month for her six-month program and wanted to charge more but was uncomfortable doing so. She consulted with another student counselor to help her raise her rates. The counselor asked Christina how it was going working with her clients. Christina said it was great. She loved working with her clients, and they were seeing many results. However, Christina was a dancer and really enjoyed working with other dancers. She didn't think it was fair to charge a lot for her program because she said dancers don't have a lot of money.

The counselor asked Christina about her favorite client and the benefits her favorite client received from the program so far. Christina began to list them: the client had lost 10 pounds, she moved out of her parents' house and got her own apartment, she began cooking for the first time ever, she quit a job she hated and got a new, better paying job, she entered a new, loving relationship and she cleared up her digestive concerns. The client was also beginning to develop a spiritual practice and getting closer with her friends. And this was only the beginning of month four!

"So," the counselor repeated to Christina, "your client has cleared up health concerns, lost weight, is cooking, moved into a new apartment, got a new job and has fulfilling relationships."

"Yes," Christina replied. The counselor asked, "Christina, how much would you pay someone to help you with all of that?" Christina replied, "$5,000." The counselor asked, "So, why are you charging your clients only $150 for your program?"

In reality, Christina was not keeping her prices low because dancers couldn't afford more than $25 a month. She was keeping her prices low because she couldn't see how much her services were worth.

We share this story with you because you probably have something similar going on. We know that what you have to offer is priceless. Your clients will change dramatically as you introduce them to healthier foods, primary foods and new cooking techniques. The high-quality listening you offer will change their lives.

Notes:

It is interesting to note that many graduates who are charging $100 a month have difficulty signing clients. However, once they raise their rates to $200 or $250 a month, people sign up without batting an eye. This change happens because the counselors did not recognize their own value, so neither did the potential clients who came to see them. If you own what you are worth, others will follow.

WHAT ARE YOU WORTH?

1. List everything that your clients get as part of your six-month program:

....

....

....

....

....

....

....

....

....

....

 ## SUCCESSFUL BARTERING

The most important thing when bartering is to make sure it is an equal trade, and that you are receiving something you want. Perhaps you'd like to trade with a massage therapist, a private yoga instructor or a web designer. A good rule to start with is an hour of your time for an hour of theirs.

It's also smart to pick someone to barter with who may turn into a referral source for you. For example, pick a yoga instructor who has a large clientele. She may share some of the things she learns from you with her clients, who may then want to come see you. Other people to barter with may include hair stylists, personal trainers, chefs, life coaches, Reiki practitioners, music teachers, language teachers or writing coaches.

Even though bartering may seem casual, it is crucial that you sign an agreement with your barter clients. This will make you look more professional, and prevent your bartering clients from rescheduling, canceling or not fulfilling their part of the agreement.

Notes:

POSITIVE FEEDBACK

One way to help you realize your value as a Health Counselor is to consistently ask for feedback. You have probably noticed that at Integrative Nutrition we ask students what they like about the calls, classes and orientations. You should incorporate this technique into your business.

At the end of each health history, counseling session or cooking class, ask the client or participants what they enjoyed. Really listen to what they say, and allow it to sink in. Also, at the end of each six-month program, ask your clients to fill out the Completion Form and the Last Session Wrap-up Form. You will be provided with both of these documents. Having your clients write down all the benefits they received from their work with you will help you comprehend exactly how valuable you are.

2. What benefits have your clients and/or friends and family received as a result of knowing and working with you?

....

....

....

....

....

....

....

3. What makes you an excellenthealth counselor?

....

....

....

....

....

....

....

THE MAGIC OF MIRRORING

Inevitably, when you are a Health Counselor, the people who seek your counseling are going through a lot of the same life circumstances you are. This is the magic of mirroring.

If you are trying to lose 10 pounds, chances are most of your clients will be as well. This phenomenon is especially true when it comes to money. If you are struggling with money, you will attract people who are also struggling with money. This is one of the beautiful aspects of being a Health Counselor. It is through counseling others that we heal our own wounds and move forward with our lives.

If you find yourself attracting lots of clients who cannot afford your program, the best thing for you to do is examine your own relationship with money. How can you open up to receiving?

DEALING WITH REJECTION

Like we've said before, on average about half the people who come to you for a health history will sign up for your program. Some graduates have a higher closing rate than others. Regardless of where you fall on this spectrum, recognize that in this business you will always have to deal with rejection. It's a good idea to put a plan in place to help you cope with any feelings that come up and to learn and grow from your experiences.

Do not be hard on yourself when someone does not sign up. Maybe that person would have been a difficult client who would have caused you a lot of strife. Maybe that person was too stuck or distracted to make a commitment to change at this time. Maybe it's not as clear as this, and you are left wondering if you could have done more.

Whatever the situation, when someone doesn't sign up after a health history, ask yourself what you might have done differently. Were you focused on the person and listening as deeply as possible? Could you have used more power statements? Do you need more verbal Kung Fu practice? Do you need more confidence when asking for money? Write down what you learned and what you want to do better next time. Then take a deep breath and move on.

It is very normal to have emotions come up when someone turns you down. You might feel sad, angry, guilty or frustrated. Remember that you are probably feeling this way because of things that happened to you a long time ago. It has very little to do with the wonderful, caring, intelligent person you are today. The only thing that has happened is that someone has chosen not to work with you at this time. Acknowledge and then let go of your feelings. Journal, make some art, go for a run, whatever works best for you. As time goes on you will come to understand that a certain level of rejection is normal, and you will not be bothered by it. You can learn from it and move forward in new ways.

GRADUATE PROFILE

LUCIA LUNA
New York, NY
lucia@lucialuna.com
2002 Graduate

After being a business owner for many years, I found myself working for someone else as a human resources manager. Although I liked the job, I was getting burnt out and dreamed of becoming self-employed again. Integrative Nutrition offered me an opportunity to create a business out of what really excited me in life.

My passion is around spirituality and personal growth. I incorporate this into my counseling practice by educating my clients about living fearlessly and becoming deliberate creators of their own lives. In addition to teaching about healthy food choices, I focus on primary food and work with clients to help them become aware of limiting thought patterns that contribute to their health concerns. I teach about the law of attraction and abundant living. Life really turns around when we change the way we think along with improving our food and lifestyle choices.

The first thing I did to start building my business was set up a neat and professional home office with the equipment I needed, mainly a computer and printer. Before I had any clients, I created a set schedule for health counseling in my planner. I made welcome packets, which contained the Health History Form and a brief outline on how my program works. I did all the prep work and back-end office tasks as a way to create space for the clients I wanted to attract.

> "...live fearlessly and become a deliberate creator of (your) own life."

I made an extensive list of everyone I knew and wrote a warm letter to introduce my practice. I sent out five to seven letters in the mail per week, so I could follow up and invite them to join me for a health history. I shared my enthusiasm for what I was up to and described to them the types of clients I was looking for.

One of the first people I talked to was my family doctor because I knew she came into contact with my niche market—menopausal women. I also met with a chiropractor and acupuncturist. I offered some free sessions to the practitioners so they could understand my work and get a taste of what I did. I ended up getting referrals from the doctor, which really jump-started my business.

One of the best tips I have for closing the deal with potential clients is to make it clear that you don't work with people who aren't committed and willing to change their lives. I explain that I am running a business, and although I would love to work with everyone, I can't because my reputation depends on results. I ask them to take a minute to decide whether they are ready to commit to making these changes at this point. If they say yes, I make the decision to work with them. By doing this, I consistently end up with clients who are a joy to work with and who make incredible changes.

Notes:

*Setting an example is not the main means
of influencing others; it is the only means.*

—Albert Einstein

CHAPTER 6:

YOUR PROGRAM OFFERINGS

Throughout our many years of experience running the school and teaching people how to be Health Counselors, we have found that the basic six-month program meets the needs of most clients perfectly. In this chapter, we will outline the components of the basic six-month program and then discuss other options, including phone clients, group programs and corporate clients.

BASIC PROGRAM

THE BREAKDOWN OF THE SIX-MONTH PROGRAM:

- Two one-hour appointments each month for six months, which will include discussion of the client's progress, recommendations and a full set of notes. You can also choose 45 minutes, if that's what you'd prefer.
- Monthly special events like a health food store tour and group discussions related to health and wellness. Remember, that this is optional, because you can simply give out the Health Food Store Tour DVD.
- An invitation to bring guests to the special events.
- A variety of handouts, recipes, books, CDs, foods and other materials.
- Email support in between sessions.

WHY SIX MONTHS?

Studies show that six months is the amount of time needed to create long-term habits. Supporting your clients for six months around making better food, exercise and lifestyle choices increases the probability that they will continue with these activities after the completion of your program. The monthly events or seminars that are part of your six-month program are a great way for your clients to meet one another and create a community, as well as an opportunity for you to meet their guests and practice your public speaking.

Giveaways

One of your program offerings is the gifts that you give each client at the end of every session. These gifts do not need to be fancy or expensive. They may include anything from cooking utensils to tongue cleaners, books to food. We will provide you with this giveaway checklist. We recommend you staple a copy of this to each client folder to keep track of what you have given to each client. You can keep a bag or a bin in your office space where you always have extra client giveaways. That way, each time you have a client, you can look in your treasure chest and pick something out. When you come across a good giveaway, buy a bunch and throw them into your stash.

Popular Giveaway Items:

- Beans
- Grains
- Recipes
- Strainer
- Thermos
- Chopsticks
- Water bottle
- Tongue cleaner
- Wooden spoons
- Organic toothpaste
- Organic tea and a tea ball
- Louise Hay affirmation cards
- Fresh greens (bok choy, kale, collards, etc.)
- *Integrative Nutrition: Feed Your Hunger for Health and Happiness*
- *The Self-Healing Cookbook* by Kristina Turner
- Blank journals for writing or using as a food journal
- Dry-erase markers (to write loving notes on the mirror)
- Condiments (umeboshi, hot pepper sesame oil, gomasio, etc.)

For giveaways including books, CDs and journals, it may be helpful to buy wholesale on Amazon.com. Their prices are already discounted and for phone clients you can have them shipped directly to them. If you are a member of Amazon Prime, then most shipping is free (annual fee of $79).

Most clients appreciate getting a binder in which to keep all the handouts that you give to them. You can purchase binders at an office supply store for less than $1 each. You may want to tape your business card to the front or insert it inside. You can give this to your clients when they initially sign up or at the beginning of their first session. It's also helpful to give them dividers for their binder so they can create sections in whatever way makes sense to them. Or you can do it for them: one section for session notes, one for recipes and one for handouts. This giveaway helps your clients stay organized around their self-care.

PHONE COUNSELING

Health counseling is just as effective when done over the phone as it is in person. Phone counseling is a great way to expand your practice and to work from the comfort of your home. It is perfect for clients who are busy, want the convenience of calling from home or the office, travel frequently, want to reduce commuting time, live outside your area or are single and/or working parents who need to be home during evening hours.

Phone counseling works well for counselors who don't have an office space, want to work from home but don't want clients there, like to travel or don't want to be encumbered with an in-person client schedule. If you like to talk on the phone and enjoy the flexibility of being able to do your sessions from anywhere, phone counseling may be a great fit for you.

If you know you want to do phone counseling, be sure to mention it in your marketing materials. Simply call or email potential clients, let them know about this new work you are doing and invite them to do a health history with you over the phone. Let them know what to expect. Tell them you will email them the Health History Form to fill out and send back to you or you'll fill it out together over the phone. Send them a reminder email or give them a quick phone call the day before your session, suggesting they put aside an hour of time in a quiet and comfortable space for your call. Consider asking them to have a glass of water or cup of tea handy.

Have your clients call you, just as if they were coming to you for an in-person session, giving them more responsibility for their session and also saving you the phone bill.

When they call in, ask them a question to create relatedness and connection. Maybe you'll ask how their day was, or something that is new and good. Make sure they are in a comfortable, quiet and private space. Proceed to go over the health history as you would in person. Ask them questions, listen and avoid giving advice.

After they've agreed to work with you, take their credit card number over the phone to hold their first official session of their program. Even if you don't have a credit card merchant account, it has them take you seriously. If are able to accept credit cards, bill them immediately for the first month. If you are only accepting checks, tell them you will need to have six post-dated checks (if they are paying in this way) and the signed Program Agreement at least 24 hours before their first session. Schedule all 12 sessions with them while you have them on the phone. Ask them to get their scheduler and put in the dates.

After you get off the phone, email them the Program Agreement, welcome letter and reminder of when their sessions begin. Encourage them to fax or mail the forms back as soon as they can.

A six-month program over the phone works almost identically to an in-person program. You meet once every two weeks for an hour, listen to your clients, provide recommendations and follow the same structure for your sessions that you would in person. At the end of each session, send them a quick email telling them how well the call went and give them the recommendations for that session. Email them any handouts you would have given them at an in-person session. Keep a record of the emails in their folder for easy reference.

We recommend that you ship them all their giveaways in two (or three) separate installments—one after they sign up for your program and one halfway through. This makes less work for you because you don't have to go to the post office each week, and it also makes your clients feel special because everyone loves getting gifts in the mail. After they sign and either fax or mail you the Program Agreement and you have their payments, mail them their first giveaway package, including their binder for the handouts and recipes that you will email them after each session. You'll also want to include one giveaway for each session through the third month—six giveaways total. Be sure to make a note of which ones you sent so you know what to send in the second package.

PHONE COUNSELING TIPS:

- Invest in a hands-free headset with mute capabilities.
- If possible, meet your client in person at least once during your six-month program.
- If you cannot meet in person, exchange photos via email or snail mail.
- Start and end on time.
- Give the client a warm welcome and check in at the beginning of the session.
- Remind them to put down any other things they may be doing, and to find a private, quiet and comfortable space.
- Begin each session with a simple breathing exercise or grounding exercise to slow their pace from the day and to be present with you.
- Do not multi-task while on the phone.
- Be conscious of the tone of your voice, and don't speak too quickly.
- Make sure the client knows you are listening.
- Ask questions, be interested.
- Don't be afraid of silences.
- Take notes.
- Direct them to the mailed giveaway that corresponds with each session.
- Email or send them a copy of the session notes page, along with the action steps you outlined, once you complete the session.

- For consistency, if you send follow-up emails to check in with the clients, you should do so regularly and at the same time interval.
- Follow up at the next session as to whether they tried the recommendations.
- Send a reminder email before the next session.

GROUP COUNSELING

Group counseling is a wonderful way for you to expand your practice and reach more people. The group setting creates a community of support and facilitates connections. It is also an opportunity for you to work with people who can't afford your individual program fees. Typical group programs are $75 to $150 per person, per month, depending on where you are with your practice. A good suggestion would be to charge half the price per month for a group that you charge for an individual program.

If you decide to start a group program, determine your target market. Is it the same target as your regular practice? Do you want to work with lower-income families, kids or men? Once you have that figured out, pick a time and location to best suit the needs of your target market. It is important to choose the start date and the session time before you begin to market the program. For example, one of our graduates runs an extremely successful group program for young corporate women at 7 a.m. on Wednesday mornings. They meet at her convenient midtown office, have breakfast and participate in group counseling for an hour and a half before work. Another decision to make regarding your group involves the time frame. Would you like to create a six-month group or have a rolling admission group program that always has open admission?

A group program is only successful if you have members in the group. The first step is to market the group. Begin your marketing efforts about six to eight weeks before the start date. You can promote your group in a similar way as you promote your other services: email offers, newsletters, through your website, at workshops, networking events and through referral partners and clients. It's great to have people spread the word about your services for you. You can even offer a referral incentive. Always remember to discuss the benefits the participants will receive from the group, in addition to the features and program details. As an incentive, you may want to offer a deadline to enroll and an early enrollment discount. (e.g., enroll by X date, and you save $100 off the total cost of the group).

WHAT A SIX-MONTH GROUP PROGRAM LOOKS LIKE:

- Choose a start date and time, as well as a location.
- Hold individual health histories with people interested, or hold one orientation for everyone who is interested.
- Have everyone sign a Program Agreement and register for the program.

Notes:

- Be sure to collect payment (credit card or check) from each participant before you begin.
- Hand out the schedule for the meetings, which should be every other week for six months.
- Follow the session outlines we provide you, and adapt them appropriately for the group.

WHAT A ROLLING ADMISSION GROUP PROGRAM LOOKS LIKE:

- Start your group once you have four people who are interested.
- You can enroll new people into the group at any time. Be sure each new person signs a six-month Program Agreement Form.
- Since you'll have new people joining the group at different times, you will need to customize the topics so they make sense to people who are just starting, as well as people who are further along in your program.
- The group size will fluctuate, but keep at least four in the group at any given time.

An ideal group size is six to 10 people. Generally, your group size should be no less than four and no more than 30 participants. With this group size, each individual will get enough personalized attention from you and you'll be compensated for your time and energy. Go about running your group similar to the individual program. You'll have one session every other week and possibly the monthly seminars (you can combine these seminars with the ones you have for your individual clients). You'll use all the same paperwork, give recommendations and provide giveaways at the end of each session. Each session should run anywhere from 90 minutes to two hours, depending on the size of the group. You can hold your groups in a private location (either free or for a low hourly rental fee), at your home, a wellness center or anywhere you have referral relationships. Meet with the group at the same time and day of each week, every two weeks, and have this schedule set before the group begins. Take payments in the same way you do from individuals; have them pay in full, post-dated checks or credit card monthly installments.

Please feel free to customize your group programs and enhance with personal touches as you see fit. Get support from your counselor, the OEF and fellow students when creating your group program.

MANAGING A GROUP PROGRAM

Place the chairs in a circle for smaller groups or in rows of semi-circles for larger groups. Encourage the participants to change seats each time and sit next to different people to receive the most value.

The group members will feel more comfortable sharing if they trust they will not be judged, and that their confidentiality will be respected. The trust may take some time to develop. Remind them that this is a safe space, and that they are welcome to be who they are, without judgment, and they will open up and reach their goals more quickly.

Call on people who are quiet and encourage them to share. Let them know that when they share they will be more likely to grow. Everyone in the group should receive individual attention from you at some point during their group program. This may be during their group shares, a Q&A or one-on-one coaching. You should make sure that all participants feel recognized as individuals. Send personal and group emails to check in, letting people know you are with them and are interested in their growth.

Oftentimes, the more vocal members of the group dominate the conversation. When this happens, thank them for sharing, and say you'd be happy to talk with them after the session but that you are on a schedule and have a lot of information to cover. You must be clear with your boundaries. Look out for those who are overly talkative, needy, show up late or are disrespectful. They are not supporting the group dynamic. Be proactive in handling these situations, but do so with compassion and understanding. At the end of your group program, you can offer individual programs and maintenance programs to the group participants.

CONDUCTING GROUP PROGRAMS BY PHONE

Similar to one-on-one phone consultations, you can also conduct group programs over the phone. We have outlined some simple steps below:

1. Review the group program outlines we provide. You will use the same session content by phone as you would in person.

2. Decide on a specific time and date when you'd like to start. Evenings tend to work well for many people, especially those who have day jobs. Keep the same time and day of the week for all 12 sessions, roughly two weeks apart.

3. Market your group program. You can do this much like you would your regular work (email, newsletter, lectures, referral partners, flyers, etc.). Remember to give yourself about six weeks to promote. Offer "early enrollment" discounts as an incentive to join and be sure to mention the benefits of the group calls. You can also expand your marketing to several different states because it's over the phone.

4. A phone group works well with anywhere from four to 30 or more people. Decide what number you are comfortable with.

5. Price the program the same as you would an in-person group.

6. Enroll participants as you would an in-person group (health histories, group orientation, etc). Accept credit card payments via PayPal, or have them send you

Notes:

Notes:

PROGRAM COMPLETION RENEWAL OPTIONS

Most clients do extremely well during group programs because a lot is covered in a short amount of time. When this is the case, some might choose to work with you one-on-one in order to continue this work in greater depth.

Offer the Individual Program to:

- Clients who enjoy a slower and more relaxed pace due to an ultra busy lifestyle and want continued support for another six months.

- Clients who have achieved amazing results in a short amount of time and want to continue with a deeper focus on their main health concerns.

- Clients who would like to work on another goal, something different from what they started with at the beginning of the group program.

- Clients who simply appreciate the value of your support and services and who desire a maintenance program.

For those that fit any of the above descriptions, you can send them the following letter when they've finished your program:

Dear (name),

I've created a few options for graduates of my group program who are interested in continuing to work with me:

Sign up for an individual six-month program. Your program cost will be a discounted rate of $_____ per month.

Create a customized program. You and I can agree upon a program that is best for you. Price to be determined.

Participate in a maintenance program. See me once a month to continue receiving support and working in a comfortable way towards your goals. Price to be determined.

I have enjoyed working with you and welcome the opportunity to continue our work together. If you have any questions, I am happy to help.

Warmly,
Counselor Name
Counselor Contact Info

checks (either the entire amount or post-dated). Provide payment deadlines, and be sure you receive payment before the start date.

7. Have each participant complete the group Program Agreement Form and send it to you before the start of your group.

8. Once a member has enrolled and paid, send them a welcome email with the following information:

   • Welcome form

   • Program schedule

   • Phone number and access code

   • Program policies (missed sessions, etc.)

   • Gratitude for their participation

   • What to expect from the program

1. Set up your group conference calls. You can use a service like freeconference.com or nocostconference.com. You'll need to create a free user account on either of these systems. During that process, you will be given a phone number for your account. You will then need to schedule calls for all 12 of your group program calls. The system will additionally ask you for the number of participants on the call. You will create a PIN (access code) for the call, and give that to your participants in the Welcome Email (see step 8). It's best to schedule all of the calls at once. If you need assistance for setting up your account, you can contact technical support for either of these services.

2. Begin and conduct your group calls. Call in for your sessions two minutes ahead of time and follow the outlines. It's best to have a headset and use a land line.

Additional tips for running your groups:

• Adapt the outlines for phone groups.
• Instead of paired shares, give more time for group shares.
• After each call, email participants the handouts and recommendations.
• Giveaways are not needed, as this takes a lot of time and expense to mail to members. You can simply give recommendations of what to buy based on the session outlines.
• Keep track of group progress and handouts on the tracking sheet.
• Make sure each participant has a buddy to contact by email between calls.
• Send group emails to check in from time to time, if you'd like.
• Send group email reminders before each call.
• Be supportive and considerate.
• Don't let the more extroverted people dominate the call.

- At the end of the group, provide options to work with you privately or in another group.
- Keep learning and growing, and enjoy the process!

COOKING CLASSES

Depending on your level of comfort in the kitchen, you may decide to offer monthly cooking classes or you may mix your cooking classes with other types of seminars. Teaching your clients that cooking healthy meals is easy and fun is priceless training. Most people today think that cooking takes hours of hard work. You know this is not true. Your clients will greatly value and truly enjoy learning how to cook with you. Please note that even if you do not have a lot of experience cooking, you can still teach an extremely successful cooking class. It's okay to show your clients that you are not an expert, but that you still manage to make healthy meals in a short period of time. We will provide you with an outline and guidelines for conducting a cooking class. If you do not offer cooking classes, you can still give your clients a copy of the cooking DVD.

HEALTH FOOD STORE TOUR

Many people are intimidated by the various products that appear on the shelves of a health food store, so they buy organic or healthier versions of food sold in the regular grocery store. Some of your clients may never have even stepped foot in a health food store. Scout out the best one in your area and introduce yourself to the manager. Give the manager your business card, explain that you are a Health Counselor and that part of your program involves giving your clients a tour of a health food store. Let the manager know how many people you'd like to bring on the tour and that it will be an hour to 90 minutes long. Explain that you'll be encouraging your clients to buy products after the tour and to come back to the store in the future to do their shopping. Most stores will be very welcoming. See if the manager can agree to offer your clients discounts on the day of the tour. Agree on a date and time with the manager and thank them.

Some of your clients may want a private tour. If this is the case, you can always substitute a health food store tour for one of their sessions. You will receive a full outline and guidelines for conducting a tour. Whether you decide to give group or private tours, be sure to watch the Health Food Store Tour DVD to familiarize yourself. For phone clients who want the tour but are too far away, you can send them a copy of the Health Food Store Tour DVD. You do not have to offer the health food store tour, and can simply loan or give a copy of the DVD to the client.

MONTHLY SEMINARS

If teaching cooking classes is not your thing, you can offer monthly seminars on other health-related topics. You can do a Sugar Blues or an Eating for Energy talk for your current clients. You can also customize seminars to fit the needs of your target market. For example, if you work with corporate clients, you may want to do a stress reduction seminar. If most of your clients are busy moms, you can do a seminar on fun snacks for kids. The options are endless. These seminars are your opportunity to explore topics that are interesting to you, while also providing your clients with additional education and inspiration.

Additional Monthly Seminar Ideas:

- **Abundance**
    - –Identifying limiting beliefs about money-making.
    - –Collages about what participants want to create in their lives.
    - –Setting new intentions about money.
- **Creating a healthy home environment**
    - –Clearing clutter.
    - –Organizational tips.
    - –Clearing negative energy (incense/smudging/salt/music).
- **Fasting/cleansing**
    - –Healthy ways to cleanse.
    - –Different forms of cleansing and fasts.
    - –What time of year to cleanse (springtime).
- **Natural beauty**
    - –Make-your-own face scrubs.
    - –Eating for healthy nails, skin and hair.
    - –Anti-aging information.
- **Slowing down for good digestion**
    - –Benefits of stress-free mealtimes.
    - –Creating a positive eating environment.
    - –Chewing practice or chewing meditation.
- **Staying healthy through the holidays**
    - –Managing family stress.
    - –Gift exemption.
    - –Importance of exercise.
- **Time management**
    - –Identifying goals, desires and priorities.
    - –Working smarter not harder (to-do lists/scheduling tips/delegating).
    - –Setting boundaries for time management.

- **Dietary theories: Ayurveda, TCM, blood type diet, etc.**
  - –Quizzes to identify type.
  - –Food and lifestyle recommendations.
  - –Choose three things from this theory to incorporate into diet or lifestyle.

You can also offer seminars that address common health concerns. Your clients are probably hearing about these and could use some education and support. Health seminar topics could include:

- IBS
- Allergies
- Diabetes
- Heart disease
- Cold and flu season
- Men's health issues
- Women's health issues

Guest Speakers

A great way to add benefit to your program, while reducing your own workload, is to invite guest speakers to your seminars. Do you know someone with their own business who can offer expert advice and demonstrate their services for your clients? They would probably be happy to speak in front of a new audience, and your clients would be thrilled to hear them. Guests will often speak for free in exchange for being allowed to give their marketing materials to your clients. Possible guest speakers include:

- Chiropractors
- Acupuncturists
- Personal trainers
- Tarot card readers
- Whole foods chefs
- Massage therapists
- Skin care consultants
- Meditation instructors
- Personal finance experts
- Yoga or Pilates instructors
- Vitamin and supplement experts

For any seminar you give, start by creating an outline. Figure out what you want to say. Then use the talk outline for Sugar Blues or Eating for Energy to help you organize your information. Leave at least 20 minutes at the end for your clients to ask questions and get support to make specific changes based on what they just learned. Practice helping your clients to support one another. You can have them do paired shares or assign buddies to check each other's progress.

SCHEDULING YOUR MONTHLY SEMINARS

Due to clients' busy schedules, scheduling can become the most complex component of your monthly seminars. When you have only two or three clients, you may try to work around their schedules, but as your client base grows this will likely be impossible. We recommend that you pick one day of the week that works best for you, and tell your clients when they sign up that your monthly seminars are always on that day (e.g., the first Monday of the month, the third Thursday of the month).

CUSTOMIZED PROGRAMS

If you are already a licensed professional, such as a chiropractor, massage therapist, personal trainer or yoga instructor, you can certainly combine your previous career with health counseling. You can add one or two massages, yoga classes or training sessions to your six-month program and increase the price accordingly. If you are interested in combining health counseling with other practices, consider offering various tiers of service. Create a handout that outlines your different program offerings.

Explain your basic six-month health counseling program and list the fee. Then list a medium-priced program that combines health counseling with one extra service each month, such as one massage or private yoga session. Your deluxe program can include two extra services each month. Make sure you give your clients a cost incentive to want to buy the more expensive programs, and let them know that they are getting a discount when they buy more. For example, if your regular program is $150 per month, you can have your medium program cost $225 per month and your deluxe cost $275 per month.

Throughout your career as a Health Counselor, you can continue to add special offerings to your basic program and see which ones your clients respond to. Other services that graduates have added to their programs with success include: monthly food shopping, private monthly cooking classes, Pilates sessions, polarity therapy and fashion consulting. Again, we recommend that you stick with the standard six-month, every-two-week format.

At some point, you will come across a client who wants extra support and asks to meet with you once a week. You may also have a client who wants to get through the whole program quickly. One week is usually not enough time for a client to try out and fully integrate the recommendations from the previous session. If you do 24 sessions, you may find yourself doing more work by creating new content for the extra sessions, And lastly, you may find yourself giving an unbalanced amount of energy to this one client. Sticking to your every other week counseling schedule allows you to keep your own life in balance and be the best counselor possible. You can explain to your client that the six-month program has proved to be very effective and that they are much more likely to have success in meeting their health goals. However, it is entirely up to you how you work with that person. Experiment and see what works best.

Notes:

CORPORATE CLIENTS

You can be successful with corporate clients even if you've never had a corporate job or worn a business suit. Working with corporations is an excellent way to get paid well and to obtain access to a large number of people who could become potential clients. It can also be profitable work for you because companies have a lot of resources.

The first step is to identify the type of corporations you want to work with. Is there a particular industry that you find fascinating, have experience with or connections to? Perhaps you have a passion for fashion, and you'd like to work with large department stores or designers. Maybe you have a lot of friends in publishing who might be able to get you into their companies. Or perhaps there is a hedge fund nearby that you'd like to become involved with. Spend a little time talking to friends about corporations they know of that might be interested. Also, research on the internet, in local periodicals, or simply drive or walk around your area and take note of companies you may not have noticed before. If you don't have a contact but have an industry in mind, you can still send an email to a main contact (see email 1).

Make a list of companies where you would like to offer corporate workshops:

1. ....

2. ....

3. ....

4. ....

5. ....

Make a list of all the people you know in those organizations or in the industry. These people are your best bet for getting connected with the person in the organization in charge of Human Resources and/or corporate wellness programs. Having a pre-existing contact will speed up the process of booking a corporate event.

1. ....

2. ....

3. ....

4. ....

5. ....

Sample Email 1: Send this email to contacts you do not yet know and have no referral for.

Subject:

Dear (include name here):

I hope this email finds you well. I want to introduce myself to (corporation name here). I am a certified Health Counselor with a focus on corporate wellness. I believe my expertise in corporate health will greatly benefit the intelligent, hard working men and women in your company and give them the tools and knowledge they need to feel less stressed and more energized to fulfill their professional as well as personal responsibilities.

As you are aware, health insurance costs continue to rise and the healthcare system appears to be crumbling. My workshops on "Stress Management Made Simple" and "Healthy Eating at Work," along with several others, will help increase productivity, decrease absenteeism, reduce the need for medical care and increase employees' desire to live a healthier lifestyle. The smartest companies know that they save money (and retain good people) if they provide wellness education and lifestyle support for their employees.

I'm interested in talking with you about how I can support you and your company. I can send you a copy of my press kit, which should explain more about my work and how I can lend my expertise to your employees. Thank you for your time, and should you have any questions, please feel free to email or call me at (number here). You can also visit my website at (your URL name here). I look forward to speaking with you.

Best regards,
Health Counselor Name

ONCE YOU HAVE IDENTIFIED YOUR CONTACTS, CALL OR EMAIL THEM (SEE SAMPLE EMAIL 2):

- Tell them that you are a Health Counselor and corporate workshop presenter.
- Let them know you have a workshop that you present to corporations, educating employees about how to make better food and lifestyle choices, as well as reduce stress in the workplace.

Notes:

- Ask them who is responsible for corporate wellness workshops or hiring speakers.
- If there is no program like this, ask for a contact in the HR department.
- Ask your contact to send an email or place a call to say that you will be contacting the company. Your contacts should state that they know you and that you have some valuable information to share about the benefits of health education in the workplace.
- It's always best to do a bit of research about the company before you contact them. Learn what they do; find out what types of wellness initiatives they may or may not have in place. You can usually find that information on their website or by doing an online search.

CALL THE NAMES THAT YOUR CONTACT GIVES YOU:

- Be professional and courteous.
- Introduce yourself and tell them you were referred to them by (contact's name), and that you would like to learn about what they are currently doing to promote health and wellness in the workplace, and how you can be of support.
- Tell them that you are a certified Health Counselor, and you present workshops to educate employees about how to make better choices for food and lifestyle, and how to reduce stress at work.
- Ask them about their company.
- Identify what their needs are and what is important for them, or what may be missing at their company.
- Tell them you would like to learn more about how you can support them in helping their employees to have a happier and healthier workday.
- Remind them of the benefits of these types of programs: reduced absenteeism, lower healthcare costs, increased productivity, improved community atmosphere and higher employee satisfaction.
- Ask if they would like to see a menu of presentation ideas you can offer their company.
- Tell them that you have an information packet that you would like to send them that describes your workshop services. Ask them where you can send it, and let them know you will do this right away and then follow up with them after they have had an opportunity to review it.
- Thank them for their time and let them know you are excited to continue learning how you can support them and their organization.

Sample Email 2: Use this email if you do have a contact

Subject:

Dear (first name of contact):

Thank you for speaking with me about your (corporation, company, center, organization) and how I can support your employees as a health and wellness workshop presenter. I appreciate your consideration.

As you are aware, health insurance costs continue to rise and the healthcare system appears to be crumbling. Studies suggest that preventative health and wellness programs help lower insurance costs, increase productivity, decrease absenteeism, reduce the need for medical care and increase the employees' desire to live a healthy lifestyle. As a Health Counselor, I provide group workshops that educate employees on how to improve their health, choose food and take actions towards living a more balanced life.

In this packet I've included a prospectus that details my services and experience as a Health Counselor, including an overview of my corporate health workshop, the benefits to your organization, my experience and a sample of my writing. Please review the information at your convenience, so that you may have a better understanding of my mission and of the work I do to support corporate employees.

I'm excited about the possibility of contributing my experience to your organization. I will contact you on (date one week later) to answer any questions you may have, and discuss when we can meet in person to plan a workshop. In the meantime, you may reach me at (your number) if you have any questions.

Regards,
Counselor Name
Counselor Contact Info

CONTENTS OF THE INFORMATION PACKET:

- Use high-quality, professional paper.
- Customize the letter to reflect your knowledge about the company.
- Customize the program offering, putting in specific information you have received about the company.

- Put the packet together: letter, sample program description, bio and newsletter.
- Include your business card in the folder (use a quality, professional folder).
- Use a footer on the documents that includes your contact info.

Follow up by phone about a week later, as promised, and request an in-person meeting. Dress professionally for this meeting. Use your charm, be considerate, and ask them how they feel you can support their employees. Figure out what needs they have and how your services can meet those needs. Discuss the different workshops you can offer, and let them know that you can do a one-time workshop or a series. Recommend a workshop you think would benefit their company, and ask what they think would best suit their needs. Tell them how much you charge for your services and attempt to schedule a time for your first workshop. It may take several rounds of approval for budget, time and planning before they confirm a date with you. Be patient, but consistent. Once you have a date in the calendar for the workshop, work with your contact person at the company to ensure that a room has been secured and their employees informed about your workshop. Be sure they are aware of your fee (as negotiated in person). Prepare for and present your talk. We will provide you with a sample outline for your corporate talks. You can also use the Sugar Blues or Eating for Energy outlines, adjusting them to make the content pertinent to the work environment.

WORKSHOP MENU

Another option is to present a menu of workshop ideas to the corporation. You can present it at the beginning of your discussions or once you have done a workshop. It's always best to start with the intro Corporate Wellness Workshop. The objective is to get a three- or six-presentation deal. Do not give them this list of ideas until you have their permission and they want to see it. Here is a sample:

- Health and Self-Nourishment
- Superfoods at Work
- Stress Management Made Simple
- How to Master the Art of Guilt-Free Self-Care
- Smart Nutrition for Busy Professionals on the Go
- Spring Cleanse: A Fast, Easy Detox for your Body and Spirit
- How to Put More "Life" Into your Work-Life Balance
- End Emotional Eating
- Finding Time for Fitness and Relaxation
- Nurture the Environment, Nurture You
- Office Yoga
- Breathing for Healing
- Weight Management

You can put a list of topics together and include it in your press kit, or provide this list to them in additional meetings as you move forward with the corporation. Be prepared for whatever you put on your menu to be selected.

COLD CALLING

If you do not have corporate contacts, you can use the internet or business directories to find listings for your favorite companies. Call anyone and ask for the name and number of the person in charge of employee wellness or HR. Get the contact information for that person, and give them a call to introduce yourself and your services.

Cold calling usually takes longer than networking, and not everyone may be as responsive to your request. Even if the company chooses not to work with you, keep them on your mailing list and thank them for their time. They may be interested in the future. If one opportunity doesn't happen, another will come along. Keep moving forward, step-by-step.

CORPORATE WORKSHOP FEE

The typical corporate workshop fee is $400 per hour-long session. Multiple sessions are priced at a discounted rate, based on the number of attendees per workshop. This fee includes all materials and handouts. You can price as you feel comfortable, though $300 to $600 per hour is the average range for our graduates. A full outline and general guidelines for conducting a corporate workshop will be provided.

SINGLE WORKSHOPS

If you've set up a single workshop at a corporation, the goal is to leave with health histories scheduled and with the participants feeling that they benefited from your presentation. You want the corporation to speak highly of you, to refer you to other corporations, and potentially invite you back for another workshop or a series of workshops.

WORKSHOP SERIES

When pitching your services to a corporation, you might want to offer three workshops—one a month for three months—or you may want to offer a six-month program with 12 different workshops.

Let the person you are speaking with know that you can do single workshops or a series. Explain that if they get a series, their employees will experience greater benefits and the company will save money.

GROUP PROGRAMS

Eventually, as you build a relationship with your corporate contact, you could conduct a group wellness program for the company employees (see "Group Programs" page 113) You could offer either a three- or six-month group program, following the general outlines for groups that we provide. This group could even be sponsored by the company and held at their location. You could negotiate a set fee per employee in the group, or perhaps a total fee for the entire group program (you can discuss details with your contact, and see how open they would be to helping you organize and/or promote it). You could also arrange your own group offsite and promote it when you do your corporate workshop. Either way, this is a great opportunity for you to help many people and significantly build your business.

CORPORATE SERIES SAMPLE LETTER

Dear (Employer),

Preventable diseases cost businesses thousands of dollars a year. Recent research shows that 35 percent of absenteeism is due to personal illness. This absenteeism costs some large employers an estimated $850,000 per year in direct payroll costs—more when factoring in loss of productivity, morale and temporary labor costs (CCH Inc. by Harris Interactive, 2006). Another survey projects that the average annual cost per employee for healthcare will exceed $9,300 in 2008 (Towers Perrin, 2008).

Both employers and health insurance plans are looking for ways to decrease these expenditures. They want employees to take greater responsibility for their health by focusing on prevention, especially with high-risk individuals who are overweight or obese. Many methods enable weight loss, but most people regain much or all of the weight back. The best way to maintain weight loss is to make easy, sustainable and permanent lifestyle changes.

Across the country, companies are beginning to take notice of the startling connections between employee wellness and fiscal responsibility, and look for better answers. Employee wellness programs not only boost morale, but also make significant, measurable differences in healthcare spending. Studies have shown that employee wellness programs help companies reduce their healthcare costs between $2.10 and $10.10 for each dollar invested!

[Your company name] is proud to present its Wellness Series, comprised of 12 programs (you can choose less if you'd like) designed to inspire employees to take significant, preventative steps for their long-term health and wellness. The Wellness Series is accessible to a wide range of people, and addresses the most common current health issues, including: low energy, stress, weight loss, high blood pressure and cholesterol and how to incorporate healthy lifestyle choices into busy schedules.

Programs in the series run 60 to 90 minutes, and trainers are highly interactive with the audience, incorporating exercises, visual aids, handouts and other media. A teleclass format is also available. This workshop series gives employees the skills to take control of their wellness by deepening their knowledge of the effect of nutrition and lifestyle changes on their health. The series is excellent training to help employees make the best choices to sustain their vitality and productivity for years to come.

Thank you for your interest in [your company name] Wellness Series. This packet contains detailed information about our 12-program series, as well as my biography and testimonials from recent clients. Please feel free to contact me for more information or to schedule a workshop in the coming months.

Sincerely,
Counselor Name

GRADUATE PROFILE

JENN EDDEN
Syosset, NY
jennedden@yahoo.com
2004 Graduate

For six years I was a manager of the Juvenile Diabetes Foundation International. For as long as I could remember I had a lingering feeling that I could be doing more with my life. It didn't help that I was always stressed out—working the corporate job with long hours, long commutes and suffering from digestive trouble.

When I nearly lost my life in an accident, I realized that I was alive for a purpose, so I began exploring what that was. Six months later I enrolled at Integrative Nutrition. Within two months I had several clients. Three months after graduation I quit my day job and started my own business as a certified Health Counselor.

My clients are super busy, overworked, stressed-out business owners and executives. They struggle with how to be healthy and balance their family and social lives. Once they see that they are choosing unhealthy foods because of their stressful lifestyles, and not because they lack willpower, they drop the "diet mentality" and begin to put better fuel in their bodies.

With my support, my clients see concrete results. They lose weight and lower their blood pressure and cholesterol. They manage their time and their stress much better. Most importantly, they stop being so hard on themselves. They are so used to functioning in a world where they are constantly being evaluated. Helping my clients redefine success is a major part of their healing process.

> "Helping clients redefine success is a major part of their healing process."

Getting support from my colleagues has been essential to my success. It is imperative to have one or two friends as your cheerleaders to run your ideas by, share what you are up to, ask for help, and get feedback and support. Also, creating simple systems for my business has helped me stay organized. I have a new client checklist, which includes a reminder to input client contact information into my computer, add client birthdays to my calendar, create a client folder with handouts and include clients on my monthly newsletter distribution list. In addition, I always make extra copies of handouts and buy extra giveaways, so I don't have to do the work every time I get a new client. Friday is my day to organize and plan for the week ahead so I can start my week off on the right foot, with time allotted for seeing clients, marketing my business and, most importantly, some down time for me!

I feel so privileged to be out there making a real difference in peoples' lives. I'm excited to be branching out into the corporate speaking arena, and I just gave my first paid talk to 15 employees. I was recently a guest on a talk radio show, The Wizard of Is (1240AM), where I was introduced as a board certified Health Counselor and was able to take calls from listeners. It felt great to be on the radio, and I know I'd even like to break into television at some point. I constantly remind myself that this is my life, not a dress rehearsal!

Notes:

*It is common sense to take a method
and try it. If it fails, admit it frankly and try
another. But above all, try something.*

—Franklin D. Roosevelt

CHAPTER 7:

MARKETING AND BUSINESS DEVELOPMENT STRATEGIES

Marketing is any method of attracting and retaining customers. It is not just your website, flyers and advertisements. It goes far beyond the tools laid forth in this book. All of your business activity becomes part of your marketing effort, including the way you set up your office, how you greet strangers, the writing of your newsletter and the clothes you put on each morning. You are your best marketing strategy, because when someone chooses to work with you, they are choosing you, your enthusiasm and energy and the benefits you offer. It's important to focus your energy on marketing. There are many options, and in order to be successful you should choose marketing activities you enjoy, as well as what will bring you the most reward.

The key to successful marketing is discovering what works for you and the personality of your unique business. Some graduates get 90 percent of their clients from workshops, while others never lead workshops and get all their clients from referral systems with other health professionals.

A number of graduates make a constant effort to get into the press and advertise frequently in holistic magazines. There is no one-size-fits-all rule when it comes to marketing. Explore the different resources available and choose what feels right to you and what produces the most results.

MARKETING REVIEW

In Chapter 4, "Finding and Keeping Clients," we introduced some of the core methods of getting clients. Here is a recap:

- Website
- Brochures

Notes:

- Newsletter
- Workshops
- Health fairs
- Target market
- Networking
- Business cards

Which of these techniques have you already tried?

....

....

....

....

....

What has been most effective for you so far?

....

....

....

....

....

....

What current marketing materials do you use regularly?

....

....

....

....

....

....

Do your materials reflect your target market, and are they in alignment with your mission statement?

....

....

....

....

....

....

What methods would you like to add to your marketing repertoire?

....

....

....

....

....

....

DEVELOPING A MARKETING PLAN

To help motivate you to stay on top of your marketing, you will need to develop a basic marketing plan. This will be a highly organized strategy for your marketing procedures. The purpose of this plan is to choose the methods that will best support your business goals, while staying within your budget. A professional marketing plan usually includes an analysis of your target market, how you'd like to be positioned in the market, an analysis of your competition, past attempts at marketing and their success rates, and your current strategy and expenses.

Marketing requires adaptation and innovation. One month your newsletter could bring in a few initial consultations. The next month you might want to design and send out a holiday postcard to everyone in your pipeline, letting them know about special discounts. Consider your marketing plan as a work in progress.

How many clients do you have now? ....

How many clients do you want to have by graduation? ....

Notes:

Who is your target market?

....

....

....

....

....

....

How would you like to be positioned in the market?

....

....

....

....

....

....

Who are your competitors?

....

....

....

....

....

....

Describe your past marketing efforts, how effective they were and how much money and time you put into them.

....

....

....

....

....

Make a list of marketing techniques you would like to try, such as getting on the radio, publishing an article, increasing word of mouth and referrals, attending health fairs, boosting your online presence or any other concept from this chapter and Chapter 4.

....

....

....

....

....

....

How and when do you plan to implement these techniques?

....

....

....

....

....

....

....

What day of the week would you like to designate as your marketing day?

....

What hours on this day will you spend on your marketing materials and events?

....

BUSINESS REVENUE PLAN

Next, let's take a moment to be more specific about your income goals as they relate to your work. When you are clear on what you'd like to make, you can have a better idea whether your goals are realistic, and then plan accordingly to reach those goals. For example, if you know you'd like to have four new clients next month from a workshop, it's important to start the marketing and planning process now, instead of waiting to the last minute. You can also decide from which sources of income you'd like to earn revenue (workshops, group counseling, individual counseling, corporate wellness).

Your business income plan can be very simple or complex. Here is a formula for a simple business plan:

BUSINESS REVENUE TRACKING 2008

	JAN	FEB	MAR	APR	MAY	JUNE	JULY	AUG	SEPT	OCT	NOV	DEC	TOTAL
PROJECTED INCOME													
INCOME SOURCE 1													
INCOME SOURCE 2													
INCOME SOURCE 3													
INCOME TOTALS													
ACTUAL INCOME													
INCOME SOURCE 1													
CLIENT 1													
CLIENT 2													
CLIENT 3													
CLIENT 4													
CLIENT 5													
CLIENT 6													
CLIENT 7													
CLIENT 8													
CLIENT 9													
CLIENT 10													
CLIENT 11													
CLIENT 12													
CLIENT 13													
CLIENT 14													
CLIENT 15													
CLIENT 16													
CLIENT 17													
CLIENT 18													
CLIENT 19													
CLIENT 20													
CLIENT 21													
CLIENT 22													
CLIENT 23													
CLIENT 24													
CLIENT 25													
CLIENT 26													

BUSINESS REVENUE TRACKING 2008 PAGE 2

	JAN	FEB	MAR	APR	MAY	JUNE	JULY	AUG	SEPT	OCT	NOV	DEC	TOTAL
INCOME SOURCE 1 TOTAL													
INCOME SOURCE 2													
SOURCE 1													
SOURCE 2													
SOURCE 3													
SOURCE 4													
SOURCE 5													
SOURCE 6													
SOURCE 7													
SOURCE 8													
SOURCE 9													
SOURCE 10													
SOURCE 11													
SOURCE 12													
INCOME SOURCE 2 TOTAL													
INCOME SOURCE 3													
SOURCE 1													
SOURCE 2													
SOURCE 3													
SOURCE 4													
SOURCE 5													
SOURCE 6													
SOURCE 7													
SOURCE 8													
SOURCE 9													
SOURCE 10													
SOURCE 11													
SOURCE 12													
INCOME SOURCE 3 TOTAL													
TOTAL ACTUAL INCOME													
INCOME COMPARED TO GOAL													

First, decide how much money you want to make from health counseling over the next year: ....

What would that work out to, on average, per month? ....

Next, figure out what you want to charge for your services. Most of our students start out at $75 to $95 per month while they are still in school. After they graduate, they typically increase their rates to $195 per month. From there, rates can go to $250 per month, $295 per month and higher.

How much do you want to charge your clients each month? ....

Now, divide how much you want to make each month by how much you want to charge your clients each month. This is the number of clients that you will need to pay you each month to reach your income goal: ....

....

(Example: You want to earn $24,000 from health counseling this year. You would need to earn $2,000 per month. If each client you work with is paying you $195 per month, you will need to have 11 clients to pay you each month.)

From here, you can plan how many health history consultations you will need to do each month. On average, 50 percent of your health history consultations will become clients. This percentage will improve as you get more experience, but this is a good number to use starting out. So if you want to get four new clients, you will need to do eight free consultations. If you do eight free consultations each month for three months, you should have 11 clients.

The next step is to determine how you will get eight people to come in for free consultations. We'll talk in later chapters about how you can do this by giving public talks, networking and other methods. Eventually, you may want to create a more detailed business plan.

See the opposite page for an example of a yearly budget tracking system. Please use this as a sample of how to track and project your income from health counseling. You will be provided this spreadsheet in class.

BENEFITS MARKETING

A very important part of successful marketing is being able to effectively communicate the benefits of your work. Something of great consequence to all your potential clients is what we call WIIFM, which stands for "What's in it for me?" All potential clients want this basic question answered. If you can answer this question for them, they will be interested in becoming a client. You have to understand a person's motivation and speak to their needs.

Often times we are tempted, when we promote our work, to talk about the "features" (six-month program, healthcare items, group sessions. etc.). Ultimately, a potential client will become an actual client if they know and find value in your services, as it relates to their needs. The types of things a person wants to accomplish by working with you are to feel and look better, and to have more joy and passion in their life. They are looking for a return on their investment from your program—whether it's to lose weight, sleep better, reduce stress or reach other more specific health goals. You have to offer people what they want, or else they will not be as motivated to sign up for your programs or classes. All of these benefits must be included in your marketing efforts, whether in person, at a workshop, during a health history, or in your written materials.

What are some of the benefits your clients receive from your work?

....

....

....

....

....

....

In what ways can you include these benefits in your marketing communications?

....

....

....

....

....

....

YOUR CORE MESSAGE

Remember back in Chapter 4 when we had you develop your elevator speech? Now we are going to take that tool to the next level. Review this formula for an elevator speech.

My name is .... I am a Health Counselor. I work with (target market).....................
who (what you help your target market with) ....

This is a dynamic way to introduce yourself, but it's only the first level. Quite often, after this introduction, people will want to know more about how you work with your clients. Please keep in mind that it's important to tailor your conversations to the person with whom you are speaking. Be careful to not talk too much, and remember to discuss the benefits of your work as it relates to that individual. If you listen and stay present, you will increase your likelihood of them attending a health consultation and eventually becoming a client. You should try to ask questions that will make them think about how they could benefit from your services (e.g., "How do you see this work being of benefit to you?") Be certain not to use any health jargon, and explain your work in a way that the person can understand it, especially how it relates to them and their life. At some point, you may want to explain that you work with clients in a six-month program designed for their individual needs in which you introduce them to new foods, teach healthy cooking and healthy shopping techniques and support your clients to maintain healthy, active lifestyles.

To help potential clients understand the benefits of your program, you can ask, "What is your main health concern at the moment?" When they respond, you can share with them how you've worked with other clients who had similar concerns by looking at how their diet affects their health. You can then offer this person a free one-hour consultation to discuss their concerns further and see firsthand how you work with your clients.

Do not overlook the importance of explaining how clients benefit from your program. For example, a Health Counselor who works with busy professional women who want to eat well and have more energy might mistakenly say, "I offer a six-month program that includes detailed recommendations, a health food store tour, cooking classes, books and handouts." This statement does not tell anyone about how these services actually help the busy professional women. A more effective way to present this information would be to say, "I work with busy professional women to incorporate healthier, more home-cooked foods into their lives. All my clients experience reduced stress and increased energy."

You will find that you adapt your message slightly, according to whom you are speaking with. For example, if the person asking you about your business is overweight, you might add that your clients also lose weight.

A significant disadvantage you face is dealing with the lack of knowledge on the part of the general public about the importance of health. Many people don't realize how much better they will feel if they start eating healthier foods and adopting different, more

Notes:

BARRIERS TO SUCCESS

- You can't decide where to begin. Marketing your business seems like an overwhelming project with too many considerations and choices. You want to make sure you do it all perfectly, so you worry about how to best spend your time. Struck by "analysis paralysis," you start and stop, sit and stew, or just do nothing.

- You aren't sure how to put the pieces together. You know you should be leading workshops, writing a newsletter and doing health histories, but you think that you should finish your brochure or design your logo or read one more nutrition book first. You don't have a system, a program or a plan.

- You can't stay motivated. With no boss holding you accountable, it's easy to procrastinate around marketing. If you don't see immediate results, you can get discouraged and lose motivation. It's difficult to not take it personally when someone doesn't sign up for your program.

If you have ever had any of these thoughts or if you are having them now, you are not alone.

People who market service businesses rarely fail due to lack of information about effective sales and marketing techniques. They fail because they don't use the information at their fingertips. Use the techniques laid out in this book, what we teach in class and the advice you get from your counselor to overcome these barriers.

Adapted from *Get Clients Now: A 28-Day Marketing Program for Professionals and Consultants* by CJ Hayden. Amacom, $19.95.

health-promoting lifestyle choices. Your marketing efforts should involve educating people around the importance of what you do. Don't assume that anyone knows what you do as a Health Counselor. Explain to people how you work with clients and how those clients will benefit from your services for the rest of their lives. You can do this in your articles and brochure, on your website, at your workshops and at networking events.

THE SALES CYCLE

Running your own business requires determination, planning and the ability to stick with it. The marketing plan you develop and the steps you take now will affect the success of your practice for both the short and long term. Often-times, business owners who do not consistently market themselves may end up in a position down the road where they are struggling to find clients. Follow the steps we've outlined to create a plan, and understand that developing a business requires that you build your visibility and trust with your potential clients and target market.

Notes:

As you build awareness of your services, stay in touch and allow people to see the value of your work as it relates to the benefits they achieve (WIIFM), and you will be more likely to succeed. Here is an example of a sales cycle: a potential client signs up for your newsletter and four months later they decide to attend your workshop; they attend the workshop and then contact you a week later for a health history; and two weeks later they begin your program.

The following strategies will help you build awareness with clients, and ensure long-term success:

- Consistently build your contact list, and always ask each person you meet to join your newsletter or email list.
- Offer frequent invitations to visit your workshops, group events or teleclasses, so people have numerous opportunities to understand how you can help them.
- Have low- or no-cost ways for potential clients to learn more about you. These may be free health history consultations, free articles, newsletters, or a free chapter of your E-book. Find ways to build community by bringing people together in groups through volunteer activities, social outings or local events.
- Always follow up with new people you meet, and stay in touch with them.
- Be consistent, stick with your plan and trust the process.

What strategies will you use to build relationships and create a successful sales cycle over time?

....

....

....

....

....

....

What steps will you take to start implementing these tools now?

....

....

....

....

....

FILLING THE PIPELINE

"Filling the pipeline" means finding ways to meet and connect with new people. The concept of filling the pipeline comes from *Get Clients Now!* by CJ Hayden. In this book, she outlines her marketing and sales system for getting clients. The first step is to fill the pipeline.

According to her principles you should focus on this stage of marketing if you are brand new in business, do not have enough people to call, have called all your prospects in the past 30 days or your prospects don't need or can't afford you. At this point you need to increase visibility and outreach. Some ways to do this are to lead a workshop, attend an event or write an article for the local paper. If you want to have a booming business as a Health Counselor, your goal should be to have a constant stream of initial health histories. To produce this desired outcome, you will need to consistently add people to your pipeline.

Marketing is a numbers game. You often have to meet, contact and connect with many people to generate an actual client. For example, you might need to meet the receptionist at a spa, then the manager, then the events coordinator when booking a workshop. At the workshop you meet all the attendees. One of the attendees may refer a friend to you who becomes a client. That is the fifth person who you've interacted with before signing this particular client. Other times, you may run into a stranger at a health food store who becomes a client right away. Anyone you meet could become a client, refer a great client to you, or know of a location or business where you could lead a workshop. The truth is you never know where your next client may come from, but the more people who know you are a Health Counselor, the more quickly your client base will grow.

Guidelines for filling your pipeline:

- Always follow up with potential clients.
- Research places near you where potential clients hang out: gyms, spas, schools, religious centers, bookstores, etc.
- Lead workshops at least once a month in various places so you are always in front of a new audience: schools, your church or temple, community centers, corporations, etc. Think big!
- Find subtle ways to incorporate your work as a Health Counselor into conversations with friends and acquaintances.
- Continue gathering phone numbers to call.
- Master outreach: newsletters, phone calls and emails to potential clients and/or referral partners.
- Increase visibility: get published, lead more workshops and add people to your newsletter recipient list.
- Try to create an association with a pre-existing company, school, doctor's office, hospital or organization that will give you consistent access to all the new people who walk through their doors.

Once you have mastered filling your pipeline, follow through with all the people in your pipeline. Add them to your newsletter recipient list, send them emails to check in, invite them to workshops or cooking classes, and keep them updated on your programs and referral systems. It can take many newsletters or multiple meetings before people are ready to work with you or send you referrals. Keep in touch with all of your contacts and stay visible. Eventually, you want everyone in your pipeline to be so impressed by you and the work you do that they share it with people they know and, consequently, clients seek you out. Remember that you will always have to put effort into filling your pipeline.

REACHING OUT TO OTHERS

Whether a wellness center, corporate contact, referral partner, doctor's office, workshop location or media outlet, it is always best to reach out in an organized and professional fashion. Your goal is to grab their attention, make an impression, show the benefits of your work and build relationships that will lead to you finding more clients and growing your business.

Steps to Reach Out:

- Make a list of people you know already with whom you'd like to build a working relationship like doctors, yoga teachers or corporate contacts.
- Make a list of organizations and people you want to get to know based on your target market and goals.
- Research the organizations to learn more about their work and to see whether they have a potential need for your services.
- Go to any events (if applicable) at these organizations to learn more about them and to make yourself a bit more known.
- When you are ready to reach out and inquire about opportunities, think about what you'd like to have happen. Do you want to be a referral partner, perhaps a workshop presenter? Be sure you are open to different possibilities.
- Make initial contact in person, by phone, or by email based on how well you know the person. Ask who would be the best person to speak with regarding any of these areas: volunteer opportunities, partnering, referrals, guest speaker engagements, program support or media.
- Contact the person in charge, introduce yourself, and ask what you can do to learn more and how you can support the organization's clients/patients/viewers.
- Ask about scheduling a meeting to learn more about the organization or person and how you can support one another.
- Attend your meeting via phone or in person, and bring support materials like your press kit. Remember to discuss your benefits.
- Ask questions to figure out how your services will fit their needs.

- Perhaps offer a health history to the person in charge and let them get comfortable with your work.
- Get your foot in the door. Find your entry point by figuring out what you can offer and when.
- Keep building the relationship and stay in touch.

REFERRAL SYSTEMS

Clients like to see professionals who come recommended by someone they already know. Not many people pick their doctors, dentists and massage therapists out of a phone book. You know when you go to a doctor, and you need a test that they can't perform, they send you to a doctor who can? That's an example of a referral system. Almost all health professionals have referral systems, because they are an effective way of getting new clients.

As a Health Counselor, you can set up referral systems with doctors, chiropractors, acupuncturists, personal trainers, massage therapists and anyone else you can think of who has clients who might be interested in your services. Directly asking for referrals is common practice among healthcare providers, so you need not be shy. We have included a sample letter/email you can send to potential referral partners. Please use this and start reaching out. (See page 148 for Referral Letter.)

The first step to setting up a referral system is to make an appointment with someone who you think would be a good referral partner. Maybe it's a chiropractor, doctor or yoga instructor. At the end of your appointment, you can mention that you really enjoyed working with them, and ask if it would be okay to send your clients to see them as well. They will probably ask what you do, and you will respond, "I am a Health Counselor. I work with (target market) who (what you help your target market with). A lot of my clients are looking for a good (chiropractor, doctor, yoga instructor). Here are some of my brochures. If any of your clients are interested in learning more about how their food affects their health, please feel free to have them call me. I'd also be happy to extend a free consultation to you so that you can become familiar with my services."

If you already have an established relationship with someone whom you'd like to invite to become a referral partner, it may be appropriate to ask that person over for tea or a meal and discuss how you might be able to help each other out. Or you can send your press kit in the mail with a personalized letter inviting the person to create a referral system with you. Our experience shows that talking face to face is more effective than sending materials in the mail.

It's important that you genuinely like and trust the people who become your referral partners. You will be sending your clients to them, and you want your clients to have a good experience.

REFERRAL LETTER

Dear (person's name),

I'd like to introduce myself. I am (your name), and I am currently studying in the Professional Training Program at the Institute for Integrative Nutrition in New York City. When I graduate, I will be AADP certified as a Health Counselor.

I am looking for a (chiropractor, physician, acupuncturist – choose the correct title) whom I can trust to refer my clients to. I am also looking for someone who would be willing to refer their clients to me for nutrition and wellness consulting. I think we would make a great team, offering our clients both (person's specialty area) and holistic nutrition, as well as wellness support.

I have a monthly lecture series that I provide for my clients and would love to present a lecture in your office to give them more exposure to you. I also offer individual health counseling, which could be an asset to your (patients, clients) and an opportunity for you to expand your practice.

Is this something you might be interested in discussing?
My website is: (fill in website)

Thank you for your work in the community. Please let me know when you would have time to talk either by phone or in person about how we can support one another. I can be reached by email at (email address) or phone at (phone number). I look forward to learning more about your work

Kind regards,

(your name)
Health Counselor

Notes:

Let's say you've set up a referral system with a chiropractor and a client is looking for one. Give them your partner's phone number. Then call or send a card to the chiropractor letting them know that your client is coming to see them. Or, after the appointment, send a card thanking them for taking good care of your client and telling them that you look forward to future referrals.

If they send you someone first, send them a small thank you gift in return. No matter how small the present is, it will make a strong impression. Good gifts might be the Integrative Nutrition book, so they can understand more about what you do as a Health Counselor, or a gift certificate to www.Amazon.com.

INFORMAL REFERRALS

Think of everyone you know. Now think of everyone they know. You have just started this new, incredible business. Today, the public tends to be skeptical. Hearing about a skilled professional first hand makes a big difference in the decision to call someone. We like everyone from our doctor to our accountant, from our house cleaner to our dry cleaner and our massage therapist to our hair dresser to come on a recommendation from someone we know. That's a lot of people. You want the people you know to tell everyone they know that you have just started this new, incredible business.

Word of mouth is one of the best, most cost-effective ways of marketing. Your current clients, friends and family can become an effective marketing team for you by telling people they know about your services. To encourage them, you can create a referral structure for non-professionals.

Take a moment now and make a list of 20 health professionals in your area whom you could partner with. Use the internet, ask for ideas from everyone you know and check out the phone book.

1. Dr. Wirth
2. Lisa Perez - Massage Therapist
3. Cheryl Martinez
4. PT - Ross, Dana, Ymane, Alex...
5. Jocelyn
6.
7.
8.
9.
10.
11.

Notes:

12. ....

13. ....

14. ....

15. ....

16. ....

17. ....

18. ....

19. ....

20. ....

Start with the first person on the list and work your way down. Make contact and give them your referral pitch. It may take a few months to hit everyone on this list, so be patient. Certainly, there has to be at least one person on this list who will be thrilled to create a referral system with you.

Talk to the social butterfly in your group of friends, your hairdresser, a local real estate agent, a restaurant owner and other people who are well connected. All of these people should know what you do so they can spread the word in their circles. The best way to fill them in is to invite them to a complimentary health history. At the end of the health history, they may sign up and they may not. If they do, great! Inevitably, they will start to change and people around them will want to know why. If they don't sign up, that's okay too. You can tell them that you are taking on new clients, and if they know of anyone who might be interested in working with you, they should send them to you. At this time, you can tell them about your referral policy.

Even if you aren't comfortable with pitching your services to your close friends and family, you can invite them for a health history, letting them know you want the practice. Once the health history is complete, you don't need to try to close the deal. Simply ask them how it was for them. Let them know that you really appreciate their time and that you enjoyed your session. You can casually mention that you are looking for clients, and if they know anyone who might be interested in hiring you, they can send them your way and you will take great care of them.

Your referral policy might involve giving the same gift to everyone who refers clients to you, or you can do it on a case-by-case basis. For instance, you might give them a book or a gift certificate for every person they refer to you who signs up for your six-month program. Or, if they refer two clients, you offer them a massage. If it's a close friend or family member, it might be appropriate for you to treat them to lunch or dinner. Do whatever feels right to you. Everyone likes to be appreciated, and when you give gifts they will remember you and most likely continue to send clients your way.

PUBLIC RELATIONS

One of the most effective ways to spread the word about your business is by getting attention from the press. Press attention gives instant credibility to your business. Many graduates have appeared on radio shows, written newspaper articles, been written up in the press and even appeared on television. These are great opportunities to increase your visibility and fill your pipeline.

Getting PR may take a little bit of research. Do some investigation into your local press. What television shows feature stories about health? Is there a popular magazine that lists the events going on in your town for the week or the month? What are all the different print publications that your target market might read? What is a hot topic in the news right now, and how can you relate it to your business? Health and wellness are huge issues in the press—everything from obesity to prescription drugs, from Medicare to the latest nutritional supplement is explored.

Contact the media to let them know you are an expert in the field of health and nutrition and that you'd like to share your knowledge. If possible, find a contact person within the organization and ask them for the protocol to submit a story or get interviewed. Some people will prefer to speak with you first, while others won't speak with you until they have seen your press kit or other information. Snail mail, telephone, email, fax and personal delivery are all functional resources when approaching the media. Give them a heads up before you send the press release or press kit, so they know to look out for it. After getting any kind of PR, send a thank you letter and maybe

REFERRAL-BUILDING TACTICS

- Attend meetings and seminars to meet new people.

- Schedule office visits. Make a date to visit your potential referral partner.

- Serve on committees. This is a great relationship-building strategy as well as a visibility strategy.

- Volunteer or trade services. Offer free health histories to all referral partners (perhaps you'd like to barter your six-month program with some of them).

- Share resources. You can share an office space with massage therapists or other health professionals, or share your contacts and email lists with them.

- Collaborate on projects. You can put together a wellness event with people whom you'd like to add to your referral network.

Adapted from *Get Clients Now: A 28-Day Marketing Program for Professionals and Consultants* by CJ Hayden. Amazon, $19.95.

a small gift to your contact person at the organization. Let them know that you truly appreciate them and that you would love to work together again in the future.

Ways to get free PR:

- Set up a health fair in your town and let the press know about it.
- Organize a charity event for a local hospital.
- Offer to write an article for a local newspaper.
- Volunteer your expertise for a radio show.
- Give a workshop at a local school.
- Post articles on the web, always including a link to your website.
- Create a blog.
- Contact organizations that you are a member of and offer to write an article. This could be your high school, college, religious or spiritual group.
- Get involved with a political issue such as school food or government restrictions on supplements.
- Have the places where you do workshops send your materials to their clients and customers.
- Contact your local television station and let them know what you are doing and that you'd be happy to share your expertise with their viewers.
- Lead workshops. Speaking in front of an audience makes you an expert.

After you send the release, follow up. Call your contacts, confirm that they received the release, and answer any questions they may have. Tell them you are interested in having this release considered for publication or announcement, and ask what the steps are to make that happen. Be courteous and professional. They may or may not publicize you or your event, but at least you are developing relationships with key individuals in the media. Relationship building is essential in promoting your business, so keep these people on your contact list, and continue to send them information.

PRESS KITS

A press kit, sometimes called a media kit, is simply an information packet about a service or person. It is kind of like an extensive resume that describes your services as a Health Counselor, provides a biography of you, shares testimonials or references, and allows potential clients or partners to have an overview of your work. The goal is to grab the reader's attention and make a lasting impression. This helps you stand out and is very professional.

Whom to distribute press kits to:

- The media.
- Referral partners.
- Doctors' offices or other complementary practitioners.
- Spas or other locations where you'd like to be affiliated.
- Organizations where you want to lecture or do workshops.

WRITING PRESS RELEASES

A press release is a one-page announcement prepared for distribution to the media about you, your services and, if applicable, a particular event. You want to give journalists information that is useful, clear, timely and interesting.

Here are steps you can follow to write a press release for a workshop:

- On your computer, design a one-page listing. At the top of the page, use the heading "For Immediate Release" or "Press Release." Below this, place your name and your contact number.

- Design a catchy title such as "Eating Sugar the Right Way" or "Increasing Your Energy Forever." The more unique your title, the more interest people will show. Place this in bold and center it on the page. You can use all caps as a way to make it stand out more.

- Write the date of the release and the city of origin (e.g., August 16, 2008—New York, NY).

- In the first paragraph briefly describe what the press release is about.

- The second paragraph describes what makes your workshop unique and interesting. Don't "sell," just make it stand out by educating readers about the event with stimulating text and intriguing details.

- Provide the actual event details in the second paragraph as well, such as the date, location and time.

- The third paragraph should be a one- or two-sentence summary about you, the workshop presenter.

- Include your contact information at the end.

- The content of the press release, beginning with the date and city of origin, should be typed in a clear, basic font and be double-spaced.

- Make it fun, timely and accurate. Throw in a fact or two to add credibility. In addition to announcing workshops, you can also design press releases about you, your work in your community or your health counseling practice.

SAMPLE PRESS RELEASE

FOR IMMEDIATE RELEASE

Contact:
Susan Smith
Holistic Health Counselor
33 Healthy Lane
New York, NY 10011
(212) 555-5654
www.susanhealth.com
susan@healthcounselor.com

Eating Sugar the Right Way

New York, NY—August 16, 2008—Before you try your next weight loss plan or the latest fad diet, come attend this informative workshop aimed at teaching you how to reduce your sugar cravings and to eat sweet foods in enjoyable ways without affecting your weight or your energy. Why suffer eating foods you don't enjoy, or buying packaged "diet food" that you really don't care to eat? The workshop will be held at Healthy Spaces, 334 Main Avenue, New York, on September 3, 2008, at 7 p.m.

This workshop explores the effects of sugar on the body. Since Americans, on average, consume 576 cans of sugar-based soda per year, causing multiple health conditions including diabetes and obesity, it is imperative to learn about healthy alternatives to improve your health and energy. Participants will gain a greater understanding of why we crave sweets, how sugar decreases our energy and the cycle of sugar addiction. In addition to understanding why we overindulge in sweet foods, participants learn what alternatives exist to the typical refined sugars we find in junk food, candy bars and other unhealthy snacks.

Susan Smith, Certified Health Counselor, facilitates this workshop. She works in New York and has a private practice, counseling clients on how to reach their goals for health, weight loss and stress reduction. Additionally, she presents workshops and lectures on living a healthy, balanced life. Please contact her for more information.

www.susanhealth.com
susan@healthcounselor.com
Phone: (212) 555-5654

Notes:

- Key people in the community—those whom have access to others.
- Corporations where you'd like to do a workshop or set up a group program.

Composing your Press Kit:

- Use a high-quality folder with pockets on each side and a space for holding your business card.

- Include your bio and brochure, as well as any flyers for upcoming workshops.

- Include a cover letter addressed to your contact person. It is best to have a pre-existing relationship with someone or have a referral since this will speed up the process and heighten your chances of success. In the letter, remind them of your reason for sending the kit, describe what you have included in the packet, and add a few nice comments about how you are excited about the prospect of working with them. Provide your contact information and tell them you will follow up with them in the following week.

- Include one to two pages that describe health counseling. You can use the text from the website provided to you by the school. Write about your approach to health and wellness, the various workshops you offer and the benefits of this work to your clients. Be creative, be concise and use bullet points to make important information stand out. Customize all information to the person or organization you are addressing. If you are writing to a corporation, for example, include information about your corporate workshops and talk about the benefits to companies who provide wellness education at work, like reduced absenteeism, reduction in health care benefit costs and healthier, happier employees. You can also include a sample newsletter or an interesting, relevant article that you or someone else has written.

- It can be helpful to add testimonials and references from current or past clients or other people who have great things to say about you and your work.

Once you have sent your press kit, you must follow up. Contact the person, confirm that they received the packet, and ask if they have any questions about the material. During this call, you should request an in-person meeting to discuss what opportunities exist for you to share your knowledge and expertise with their organization. Use this as an opportunity to build relationships.

YOUR BIO

When you do workshops or present yourself to a corporation, doctor's office, wellness center or exercise studio, you will often be asked about your background and qualifications. This is the purpose of your bio. It is a portal into your life experience and a condensed version of your career history. It provides your readers with insight into who you are. It can demonstrate your credibility and detail what sets you apart from others.

You should include the bio on all your marketing materials, including brochures, newsletters and flyers.

In most cases, your bio will only be a few sentences. After all, your marketing materials should be more about your clients than about you. The bio should be short, relevant and to the point. It is helpful to have a friend or colleague edit and proofread your bio for readability and grammar.

Your Bio May Include:

- Your education.
- Awards you have received.
- Something personal about you.
- Special associations you may belong to.
- Your mission statement or business philosophy.
- Any specialized training, certification or licensing.
- Experience you've had (mostly relevant to what you're doing today).

ADVERTISING

You are probably wondering what the difference is between marketing and advertising. The answer lies in money. It's advertising when you pay to spread the word about your business, whether it's on the internet, in a magazine or on the radio. If you write an article for a magazine or do an interview on the radio without paying anyone, that is marketing. Two-thirds of the small businesses in America today operate without any advertising, using marketing alone.

Although some of our graduates find that advertising brings them a few clients each month, we have found that it is not generally effective for Health Counselors. People are more likely to work with someone they have met or been referred to, and consumers are so overwhelmed with advertisements that they often don't remember them.

If you do advertise, your best bet is to take out a small ad in a local trade journal or in a healthy living publication. Classified ads are an easy and inexpensive way to try it out.

If you are computer savvy, you can also try internet advertising. You can purchase banners on other people's websites that display a catch phrase and your contact information. You can buy certain words from search engine companies so that your website comes up on the right hand side of the page when people search for those particular words. For example, if you purchased the words "holistic" and "nutrition," your website would come up when someone typed those words into the search engine. Your choice of key words to purchase is crucial, and you'll have to pay the search engine company each time someone clicks on your link. (The links that come up on the right are paid for. The ones that come up on the left are not paid for, but are generated from the search engine algorithm that factors in the content on your site and its domain name.)

SAMPLE BIO

QUALIFICATIONS

(your name)
Certified Health Counselor

TRAINING AND EDUCATION

The Institute for Integrative Nutrition, New York City
Professional Training and Certification Program

(list other education you have here, including complimentary therapies, university, certification programs, etc.)

[place your picture here]

CERTIFICATION AND ACCREDITATION

American Association of Drugless Practitioners (AADP)
Board Certified and Accredited Member

(list any other certification you have)

OTHER EXPERIENCE

(here you should list any places, organizations, or centers where you have conducted workshops or presentations or where you do holistic health counseling, health histories, or group programs)

XYZ Community Center, New York
Workshop Presenter

PUBLICATIONS

Holistic Health Articles and Newsletters
Used for distribution to clients and email subscribers

(if you have had any other information published, please insert that here)

Contact Information
Phone: (212) 222-2222
Email: you@you.com
Website: www.you.com

Notes:

BIO EXAMPLE

Jane Smith is a Certified Health Counselor and loving mother of two. She decided to become a Health Counselor to fulfill her passion of working with children and parents to improve their health and build vibrant families. Jane received her training at the Institute for Integrative Nutrition in New York City and is certified by the AADP. She offers individual health and nutrition counseling to parents and families, is a group workshop presenter and a published author.

Use the space below to brainstorm for your bio. Don't worry about complete sentences or perfect grammar. Just get the ideas flowing!

Where were you born and raised?_____

What is your education, special training, certification, licensing (HC and AADP)?
_____
_____
_____

What associations do you belong to?
_____
_____
_____

What awards have you received?
_____
_____
_____

What unusual experiences have influenced you?
_____
_____
_____

What sets you apart from everyone else? What's something fun, unique, interesting or quirky about you?
_____
_____
_____

What specifically do you provide for your clients?
_____
_____
_____

You can create great content on your site so that search engines pick it up and other sites want to provide a link to your website. To submit your site to Google, visit ww.google.com/addurl. Another option is Open Directory, which will list you on multiple search engines. Please visit www.dmoz.org/add.html and follow their instructions. Microsoft has a fee-based service to assist you with promoting your site on the web; visit bcentral.com for more information.

Having your URL appear in website listings is a complicated process, and it entails having the proper key words and code (programming behind your web pages) embedded in the text of your site. Again we recommend that you work with an experienced professional who can design the pages for you and optimize them so that you get maximum exposure.

To learn more about increasing traffic to your website, there are many books you can read or you can simply type "increase website traffic" into a search engine and see what comes up.

INTERNET PROMOTION

Almost every business, from the corner bakery to major corporations, is harnessing the power of the internet for marketing. It is important to stay current with your marketing strategies as a Health Counselor and find simple yet effective ways to use the internet to your advantage.

Begin by using the website we give you. Make sure you put the URL on your business card, and list it in every letter and email you send. You can also send your URL to all of your contacts and referral partners, letting them know you have a site with valuable information about your services. Your website can educate potential clients, provide them with additional information after an in-person meeting, and motivate them to take action to find out more about you.

Talk about your website when you give workshops, since having one shows you to be credible and organized. Mention it in your newsletter. You can promote your services and have readers visit your site for more detailed information and to learn how to schedule a health history. Additionally, you can ask your colleagues and referral partners to mention your work and your website address in their newsletters and on their websites. At some point, you may also choose to develop your own website. Use a qualified and trained web designer, as your site should be professional and persuasive. But we caution you to not spend all your time and money designing a fancy website. Marketing is important, but getting out there doing this work and meeting people is more important.

Try this experiment, if you haven't already: Google yourself and see what comes up. If nothing comes up, or if the first few hits are not related to health counseling, you may want to increase your visibility on the web. People today Google everything. If you meet a prospective client and tell them all about your business, and then they can't find

Notes:

any information about you on the web, they may question your credibility. Increasing your visibility on the web is easy. You can write an article for a website and be sure to include your full name, website and contact information. You can also hire a newsletter company to send out your newsletter each month and archive your past newsletters on the web for you. Constant Contact or other similar services can assist you.

Your referral partners may also have a newsletter that they send out to their patients or clients. Ask them if you can advertise your services in this newsletter. For example, your friend Susan is a chiropractor, and sends out a monthly electronic newsletter to her patients and contacts. She may have a section in the newsletter to promote other services and products. You could contact her and inquire about her interest in promoting your work or one of your workshops to her subscribers. If you have a good relationship with Susan, it's likely that you'll be able to promote your work to many more people.

Besides your referral partners, do a search for other electronic newsletters that are being read by your target market. For example, you could do a Google search on "wellness centers" in your local area, to see which websites come up. You can then subscribe to the newsletters, and see if it is a potential source for you to advertise. Many individuals and organizations will allow others to advertise, either for free or lower cost. Begin your search on a couple of directories, to see which of them are best suited for your target market. To get started check out: www.new-list.com and www.ezine-dir.com.

Another way to promote yourself online is to join networks such as Facebook, MySpace, LinkedIn, or Plaxo. Remember it is all about bio-individuality, so not one site will work for everyone. Play around to see which one works best for you and your business. These sites are a great ways to establish your business and connect with old and new friends.

FACEBOOK

Facebook provides a clean, user-friendly platform for you to reach out to friends and acquaintances about your business. To set up an account all you need is an email address. Once you set up a profile, start inviting friends. Facebook protects the privacy of each user so they will have to accept your invitation. For your business, you will set up a page which is under the applications section. Be aware that your profile is the backbone to your business page. You will categorize your business depending on your services. Similar to how you invite people to be your friend through your profile, you can invite your friends or new people to be fans of your business. There are hundreds of applications that will help you best sell your brand and your services. Some suggested applications might be: discussion board, video, photos and events. For example, if you are giving a Sugar Blues talk you can put in the location, time and description in the "event" and your fans will know when you are giving your next talk. If the event was taped, you can upload the video using that application. Just as you update your brochures every once in a while, it is key to log on to your page to send updates to your fans so your business will show up in their profile's "newsfeed" section. Check out Integrative Nutrition's Facebook page for tips on other applications to add. Log onto www.facebook.com to get started.

Notes:

MYSPACE

While there are a lot of similarities between Myspace and Facebook, there are also some key differences to point out. To create a business page in Myspace you do not need to set up a profile as you would with Facebook. You can also personalize the background with a unique wallpaper theme. Does your brochure or business card have a color that you also want on your Myspace page? A unique application to Myspace is the slideshow. You can upload pictures from several different events to give people a taste of your services. Check out Integrative Nutrition's MySpace page for ideas. Go to www.myspace.com to set up a profile.

LINKEDIN

The above sites are not only for marketing your business but also staying in touch with friends and family. LinkedIn is primarily for business contacts. Think of it as an online Rolodex. In order to set up a profile you must put down a business name and category. When you set up your profile, summarize your professional accomplishments so former colleagues, clients and partners can easily find you. Your network consists of your connections (former colleagues, clients and partners) and their connections, linking you to thousands of qualified professionals. You might want to consider setting up a LinkedIn profile as well as a Myspace or Facebook page, so you will also have a place to publicize your events. Go to www.linkedin.com to get started.

PLAXO

Plaxo is another way to stay connected with friends, family and colleagues, but with more features than LinkedIn. As soon as you set up your account your email address book is automatically downloaded, so you can easily connect with everyone. Plaxo allows you to sync your profile to your blog, Facebook page, pictures, and more, so your contacts can simply click on your name to find out everything you are doing. Check out www.plaxo.com to find out more or to set up your account.

BLOGS

Consider creating a blog, which is short for web log. A blog is a kind of online journal in which you can write about yourself and whatever else you wish. If you are going to use this as a marketing tool, update your blog regularly to provide current health-related information. That way, if someone is searching for that information on the web, they will come to your blog and learn about what you do. This is probably the fastest way to get you up on the web. Go to www.blogger.com, www.blogonion.com or www.

typepad.com to learn more about how to create your own blog. It's quite simple. You'll just need a photo, your bio and the ability to regularly update your blog.

What are some ways that you want to enhance your business presence on the web?

....

....

....

....

....

....

REFERENCES

You will find that some potential clients—individuals, corporations and organizations—want to hear from people who are familiar with your work. They are interested in working with you but want to get a second or third opinion before hiring you as their Health Counselor or workshop presenter. This is when it is useful to have references on file.

After working with clients and organizations—especially those who were raving fans—ask them to write a two- to four-sentence paragraph highlighting your unique qualities and the benefits they received as a result of your work together. Build lasting relationships with these people and organizations because they will become your professional references. Maintain communication, send them your newsletter, keep them up to date on what is happening with your business, and invite them to some of your workshops and seminars. This way if they are called as a reference, they've had recent communication and know the latest news about your business.

If you lack experience in a certain area that you'd like to break into—such as corporate workshops or leading school seminars—donate your services for the first few times. Gain experience, build relationships and collect references. You can add all these references to your bio and press kit.

Create a reference handout that includes client feedback, a list of organizations where you've given workshops and any other education or achievements that are relevant. Perfect references are past clients or clients currently in your six-month program, referral partners, organizations where you've led workshops and corporate clients. If you don't have many references at this time, think back to your education, work experience and achievements. Who could vouch for your skills as a Health Counselor? Perhaps an old friend or a family member who is familiar with how much you know about food or a fellow student from Integrative Nutrition could write your first references. Ideally, they are from people who have direct experience with you as a Health Counselor. Know that these references will come with time, as you build your practice. If you're not ready to put the contact information for your references on your handout, you can simply note that they are available on request.

List some people or organizations that could be your references:

1. ....

2. ....

3. ....

4. ....

5. ....

6. ....

CLIENT TESTIMONIALS

Client testimonials are when your current and past clients share their success stories, potential clients relate to you and your work. Hearing about the success that other people have had in your six-month program will motivate potential clients to work with you.

How to Gather and Use Testimonials:

- Think about your best current or past clients, who have had the greatest success and achieved tangible results.
- Contact these clients, tell them how much you enjoyed working with them and let them know that you are looking for some testimonials.
- If they agree to do it, thank them and let them know what your deadline is. It is best to give people about a week.
- Have them write one to two paragraphs about working with you, the results they achieved, where they were before they met you and where they are now.
- Edit their text and check for grammar and spelling.
- Show the client for their approval.
- Place the testimonial on one page, with the client's name, age and profession at the top. Use a picture of them if they are comfortable, but if they are worried about confidentiality, just use their first name.
- Upload your testimonials to your website.
- Gather as many testimonials as you can and store them electronically.
- Create a binder full of all your testimonials to show potential clients, organizations and referral partners.
- Arrange several testimonials on one page to hand out to workshop attendees as a quick reference.

Notes:

- Have organizations you worked for or where you held workshops write testimonials for you.
- Include one or two testimonials on all of your marketing materials, newsletters, brochures, flyers and press kits.

Who are some people you know of who could write you a testimonial?

1. ....

2. ....

3. ....

4. ....

5. ....

6. ....

WRITING

Writing articles, newsletters and columns are great tools to gain visibility and generate publicity about your practice. Being a published author demonstrates that you have knowledge, while assigning authority to your name and your business. It allows you to communicate with many potential clients and spread your message to hundreds, if not thousands, of people. Writing an article or column in a specific periodical is an excellent way to reach your target market, publicize your business and position yourself as an expert.

Start practicing writing in your own monthly newsletter. Notice what topics you most enjoy writing about and what content comes the easiest to you. Perhaps you love writing recipes or you prefer to write about primary food. Write about what you know best. You can write about anything, really. Once you have some writing experience under your belt, you can start to send articles to local newspapers, magazines and webzines. Perhaps you'd even like to write a monthly or weekly health advice column.

Don't rule out writing as a marketing method simply because you don't think you are a good writer. There are many writing coaches and copy editors out there who would be happy to help you for as little as $15 an hour.

When approaching publications, you can either send them an article to see if they'd like to publish it, or contact them and say that you'd like to write an article for their readers. Suggest a topic you think is pertinent and see how they respond. Once a topic is agreed upon, find out your deadline and start typing.

Tips for Writing Effective Articles:

- Write about topics that will interest your target audience and relate to their needs.
- Write about topics that you know personally.
- Don't give away too much in the article. Give people just enough so they feel they've learned something, but they want to know even more.
- Make the article easy to read, with useful content.
- Spell check, edit and proofread. It's usually best to have someone else proofread for you.
- If possible, become a regular writer for one or more publications so that over time you build relationships with your readers.
- Do research to find out what the hot topics are for your target audience.
- Practice makes perfect. The more you practice writing, the easier it gets.

How to Write an Article:

- Identify a problem your target audience is experiencing.
- Consider how you can offer a solution to their problem.
- Brainstorm ideas for the article on a pad of paper or your computer, writing down everything that comes to mind.
- Create an outline, a master layout of your article from start to finish that contains your thesis, supporting ideas and information, and closing paragraph concept.
- Think of a catchy title to grab readers' attention.
- In the first paragraph, ask a question or two that helps the readers relate to your article and has them interested in reading further (e.g., "Are you tired of being addicted to sugar?," "Do you have a huge decrease in energy every afternoon?").
- Include interesting information, valuable facts and some pieces of simple advice in the body of the article.
- Use humor if possible or keep the tone light, as many people take health too seriously and are looking for a new approach.
- End the article with a conclusion, as well as an invitation to call you or visit your website to schedule a free health history.
- Edit the article two or more times before publishing, making sure you have enough time in between edits to come to the page with a fresh, sharp mind.

How to Distribute Your Article:

- Send it to your contact list.
- Place it on your website or in your newsletter.
- Build a database of editors. Identify magazines, newspapers, online publications and other periodicals that relate to your expertise and target market. Call those publications on your list, get the email addresses and contact information of

editors who are responsible for the area you write about, and find out who's in charge of article submissions.

- Send a cover letter, along with a copy of your article, to those contacts. Give them a week or so to review, then follow up with a phone call to talk. Answer any questions and see what possibilities exist for being published in their periodical. ,

- Send extra articles to your colleagues and referral partners. Have them distribute the article, along with your contact information, to their mailing list.

- Submit your article to any article directories on the web (do a Google search for "article directories).

WRITING AND PUBLISHING A BOOK

Starting a new career as a Health Counselor, whether it is full-time or part-time, is a huge undertaking. If you are committed to growing your health counseling business, then maintaining focus is crucial. If writing a book is something you desire to achieve, we definitely support you in this endeavor. However we recommend that you wait to write a book until after you have a few years of health counseling experience. Writing a book is an enormous project and will demand a lot of your time and energy. Your experience of working with clients will be instrumental in guiding you towards what kind of book you'd like to produce and the most effective way to introduce your material to the public.

Being an author of a published book is a major accomplishment and one that, although not easy, is incredibly rewarding. Writing a book is a great way to increase your credibility, boost self-esteem and gain respect. Anyone who doubted your ability to be successful as a Health Counselor will eat their words when you give them your first book.

Although we do not recommend you write a book at this time, you can begin to think about what you might like to write about. Think of a subject that you are an expert in and that people want to know about. These days, narrow topics are the best, so writing a book about nutrition may not be specific enough. What are your specialties? Who is your target market? What information would be most useful to them?

Once you know what you'd like your book to be about, create a detailed outline. This should contain all the major topics in your book, along with the supporting information you need to get your point across most effectively. You can organize your outline by chapter or by topic.

Know that your outline will change once you start to write. When your outline is in good shape, you can start to investigate publishing. Your two main options are to self-publish your book or to find a publishing house. There are benefits and drawbacks to each. In self-publishing, you maintain all the control of your book including, the content, design and marketing scheme. The major drawback is that you foot the bill and you will have to do all your own marketing and sales. But you also get to keep all of the profit. When going with a publisher, they pay for everything and invest their resources into marketing your book. However, the publisher also has final say over the content, look and feel of your book. Since the publishing house paid for everything, you will only receive a portion of the profits when your book is sold.

If you decide to self-publish, you can start to write your manuscript. When your book is about halfway done, you should find a book designer and printer you would like to use. You will also have to secure a proofreader and indexer. You can work with self-publishing services, such as authorhouse.com, that provide editing, design, promotion, printing and marketing services for a fee. Check bookstores and the internet for many reference guides on how to self-publish.

If you'd like to work with a publishing house, you should write your book proposal shortly after completing your outline. You do not want to write your book first because the publisher may steer you in a different direction than you would go on your own. Know that there are many books out there about how to write a killer book proposal.

Brainstorm possible topics for your first book:

1. ....

2. ....

3. ....

4. ....

5. ....

6. ....

BRANDING

Quick, think of Coca-Cola. Now think of Nike. Now Verizon. All of these companies have a clear and consistent brand. You know what they look like, what they offer and you can recognize their logos anywhere. Some people mistakenly believe that the key to branding is putting a lot of resources into advertising. Actually, the best way to build a solid, recognizable brand is to build a look and feel to your business and consistently deliver high-quality services.

Branding is not a necessary element of having a successful health counseling business. Many graduates do not even have a logo or brochure for their practices, and their practices are full. If developing a brand is overwhelming or not interesting to you at this time, skip it. You can always come back to this section in the future.

If you are interested in building a recognizable brand, start with your company name. Then create an attractive logo that complements your company name and uses colors that inspire you. Ask yourself if your materials send a clear, consistent message about who you are and the services you offer.

Start to use your logo and company name on all your materials, from your business cards to your newsletter, from the handouts given at lectures to your website. You want to increase familiarity. The more people see your brand, the more they will begin to accept your business's credibility.

SEASONS IN HEALTH COUNSELING

An effective way to plan your marketing strategy is to understand which business activities are most effective at which times of the year. The best months for lectures and signing up clients are January, March, April, May, October and November. You can plan for this cycle by offering special holiday gift certificates in November and December. Book a lot of public speaking events for early January through May. Likewise, use the summer months to coordinate events for the fall.

December is usually a slow month for Health Counselors. People are busy with the holidays and are spending a lot of money. It may be in your best interest to hold off doing health histories with people until mid-January, once the chaos of the holidays has worn off and regular life has been restored. You may want to use December to work on updating your marketing materials, press kit and website. This is a great time to book workshops and seminars for the coming year as well as schedule some down time or vacation time for yourself. Saying all this, however, there have been Health Counselors who have a lot of success in December and end up signing on a lot of clients. Always keep your options open.

In the summer, even though many people go on vacation and become more relaxed, you can still be proactive around building your business. Maintain momentum by utilizing unique summer resources. You can lead workshops at summer camps, teach cooking classes, organize a weekend retreat to the beach or the woods, attend health fairs or create a group program that meets outside and helps clients get fit for the beach. Be creative!

Don't forget that part of being a Health Counselor is walking your talk. Rest, relaxation, fun and play are vital to creating health. Therefore, it is highly recommended that you take some time off in the summer. Even if you don't go anywhere, it is healthy to take a break from work for a week or two. You can let your clients know in advance that you are going on vacation, and that their program will pick up again when you get back. Explain that this extends the length of their six-month program. By taking time for yourself, you are demonstrating through example the importance of balance to your clients.

FINDING THE TIME FOR MARKETING

Sometimes people say they don't have time to do marketing. What they usually mean is that they feel blocked or confused about how to do marketing in an effective way. Marketing is so important because it helps people find you, so you can help them. Here are some tips for how to make time for marketing:

- Make a list of your marketing tasks and identify what you need to do to reach your goals.
- Commit to marketing tasks and then schedule them. For example, if you send out a newsletter, choose a day in your calendar each month to create it and send it out. Then stick to it.
- Pick times for marketing and do your marketing activities at the same time and day each week. Make it your marketing hour or marketing day. For example, Monday afternoons could be your time to call wellness centers and corporations about doing talks and to send out your press kits.
- Do one thing at a time. Taking on too much at once could thwart your efforts. Focus on one area of marketing at a time: writing, networking, teaching workshops or boosting your presence on the internet. Break down each task into smaller tasks. Once one task is complete, you can add something new.
- Give your time to others as well as your materials and newsletters. When you give, you will receive.
- Build a group of people to support you with your marketing. You can use your counselor, fellow students and helpful friends and family.

DO WHAT COMES NATURALLY

When deciding which strategies are most effective for your business, strongly consider what you enjoy doing and what comes naturally to you. Some marketing techniques will be second nature, while others will feel like pulling teeth. Perhaps you don't enjoy writing, but are an excellent cook and love teaching cooking classes. You can ask around at school and on the OEF for another counselor who would like to help you with your writing in exchange for you helping them learn how to teach a great cooking class. If you absolutely hate leading workshops, the people who attend are going to sense it, so it will not be an effective marketing tool for you. You should discover what kind of marketing you enjoy, and do it often. The more natural and creative your marketing techniques, the more success you will encounter.

Notes:

SIX MARKETING TIPS

1. YOU CAN AVOID ADVERTISING

More than two-thirds of the profitable small businesses in the U.S. operate without advertising.

Concentrate on creating a high-quality product that your customers will rave about, spreading the word. Plan marketing events that keep customers involved and get positive media attention for your business.

2. DRIVE CUSTOMERS BY NEED, PRICE AND ACCESS

Need: When you're considering how to market, determine why customers need your products.

Price: Consumers like prices that are clear, easy to understand and not hidden.

Access: If cost and quality are equal between you and another provider, customers usually patronize the one that's easiest to access. How easy is it for customers to find you?

3. GO GUERRILLA

Guerrilla marketing requires time, energy and imagination, but not a lot of money. Jay Levinson's Guerilla Marketing was the first marketing book aimed squarely at small businesses. Levinson is a proponent of simple marketing devices, such as brochures, signs and low-cost public events like seminars and free consultations.

4. MARKETING IS A SENSORY EXPERIENCE

Marketing is a lot like dating. You're trying to get somebody interested and then retain their interest while you figure out if you should work together. Much of the attraction is based on the sensory experience—how your business looks, smells and the sense of order it instills. Don't underestimate the importance of a clean and uncluttered environment.

5. YES, THE CUSTOMER IS (ALMOST) ALWAYS RIGHT

One of the least expensive, most effective marketing techniques is to adopt customer-friendly policies. Your customer service program may include mailing cards, listening without interruption to any complaints, or providing extras for your clients.

6. WORDS THAT SELL

When writing copy for your marketing materials, use words that sell and inspire. Make the most effective use of your words. Look at your copy from the customer's perspective. Don't fill your copy with empty statements or superfluous information. Using too many superlatives, such as "amazing," "incredible" and "fantastic" may hinder your credibility. You may want to check out Richard Bayan's *Words That Sell* for more information on how to write effective marketing copy.

Adapted from *Whoops! I'm in Business: A Crash Course in Business Basics* by Richard Steim and Lisa Guerin. Nolo, $19.99.

MONTH-BY-MONTH MARKETING AND SEMINAR IDEAS

JANUARY	New Year's Resolutions Getting back on track health-wise Back to basics (water, breakfast) Hibernation is not just for bears (self-nurturance)
FEBRUARY	Sugar Blues Talks - Valentine's Day! Self-Love: You don't need a significant other to celebrate heart day Mardi Gras celebrations: Colorful and healthful foods to enjoy to your heart's delight
MARCH	Beating the winter blues National nutrition month Managing seasonal allergies/hay fever
APRIL	Spring cleaning: cleansing and fasting Harvest time for grains
MAY	Mother's Day Celebrating your womanhood Live/raw foods May Day: Celebration of fertility (flower baskets/outdoor gathering)
JUNE	Outdoor activities and exercise Weight management Prepare your body for summer Father's Day: celebrating men
JULY	Summer eating and keeping cool Travel time Making healthy choices on the road Independence Day: Multinational celebration (U.S., France, Canada, Philippines, Venezuela, Argentina, Belgium, Peru)
AUGUST	De-junk your kitchen Harvest
SEPTEMBER	Back to school Snazzy snacking (brown-bagging: it is not just for school kids) Noshing for energy, taste and fun Stocking up your pantry Simplifying shopping Spirituality connection: Jewish holidays Preparation for seasonal change: fall is a typical fasting and detoxification season
OCTOBER	Deconstructing cravings Fall foods True Halloween treats, sans refined sugar tricks Transition: Changing of the leaves, days become shorter Vegetarian awareness month
NOVEMBER	Holiday preparation Surviving the holidays Self-nurturance Slowing down with the season/shorter days Flu season: boost your immune system
DECEMBER	Holiday celebrations: Christmas, Hanukkah, Kwanzaa Healthy gift-giving Eating for energy

Please keep in mind that you are your best advertisement. You are a walking billboard for your business. Your health and happiness are instrumental in generating business, so don't waste precious time doing things that make you unhappy. The more you are focused on doing what you love, the more you are out and about looking like your radiant self, the more people will want to know who you are and learn how they can get some of what you've got.

FACING YOUR FEARS

We've designed this book and the Fast Track Program to provide you all of the marketing tools you need to build your business. Marketing knowledge will not be enough if you lack the confidence to make it happen, or if your fears are getting in your way. The following thoughts and feelings can hold us back: self-doubt, lack of confidence, confusion, jealousy, comparison to others, anger, fear and not feeling worthy. We are all human; it's normal to have a fear of the unknown, especially if you have never done this work before. Ultimately, our fears are behind everything that holds us back. We wonder whether we will be successful, whether people will like us, whether we know enough, if we will succeed financially etc. Fear is only in our minds though, and it's up to you to choose how you respond to it. Fear can either paralyze you or you can use the energy to push yourself forward. Our fears sometimes give us a false sense of safety, but in the long run they keep us stuck. To be successful you must take steps to get support to face your fears and build your confidence, so that you can achieve all of the success you truly desire.

Try the following exercise to help you work on any fears you may have about doing this work.

What is one fear you have around doing this work (e.g., knowing enough, public speaking, financial success, etc.)?

....

....

....

....

....

....

....

....

When you really examine this thought, do you absolutely know that the thought is true or will come true?

....

....

....

....

....

....

What is it costing you to hold onto this fear (e.g., peace of mind, not enough clients)?

....

....

....

....

....

....

What are the benefits of letting go of this thought (e.g., you'd be able to take action to find more clients)?

....

....

....

....

....

....

What are three to five actions you can take to reduce this thought, and move forward anyway?

....

....

....

....

....

Notes:

FACING YOUR STRENGTHS AND WEAKNESSES

We all have fears, and we all have strengths and weaknesses. In this next exercise, pinpoint your strengths and weaknesses, as well as what might get in your way to achieving the success you deserve as a Health Counselor.

SWOT ANALYSIS

SWOT is an acronym for strengths, weaknesses, opportunities, and threats. Using this analysis enables individuals and businesses to clarify what direction to move in by being aware of where they are and where they have the potential to go. After filling out this table, you can use the aspects you have realized to create an action plan for yourself.

Strengths What you are best at, where you excel, your resources and/or experiences
Weakness What you do poorly, what do you lack, what is not working well
Opportunities   What opportunities are coming your way, where do you see potential
Threats What could get in the way, what obstacles or problems do you foresee

	STRENGTHS:	WEAKNESSES:
INTERNAL		
EXTERNAL	OPPORTUNITIES:	THREATS:

GRADUATE PROFILE

AMEET MATURA
Brooklyn, NY
theintuitivecook.com
2006 Graduate

> "Find what excites you and work with that, leverage it and market it."

Integrative Nutrition was a life-changing experience. I now have a career and a business, The Intuitive Cook, which I never envisioned I would have. Along with my big career change, my spirituality, relationships and personal health have all improved.

The most important thing I learned from Integrative Nutrition was to be myself. As soon as I started to bring myself into my practice the more success I had. If you are yourself, then you will automatically attract the right clients.

Find what excites you and work with that, leverage it and market it. I was a fan of the Iron Chef, so I created the Great Squash Cook-Off. This community event was a contest to create a delicious vegan dish using one common ingredient: winter squash. People throughout Brooklyn submitted recipes and we chose 20 people to prepare their dish for our panel of local restaurant owners and food authorities. The cook-off was hosted at a restaurant in Park Slope, Brooklyn and the winner received $200 and the recipe was added to the menu. The event was featured on NBC, on a full page spread in *Time Out* magazine and several other media outlets.

Another marketing tool that has really worked for me was building a referral network with health practitioners and Health Counselors. Creating a referral network with people that know you and that can connect you to people that excite you is key. Marketing can be very low-tech because it's about establishing a connection with people.

After PTP, I did health counseling alone and it was really tough. Once I applied for immersion, I started to get the support I needed to develop my business.

Before coming to Integrative Nutrition, I was a senior marketing associate and product manager of a large food company. I have always been passionate about food, but my job was never about the food; I was just selling products.

My first introduction to holistic nutrition was when my mom gave me a book by Andrew Weil. I fell in love with it. I started looking at traditional nutrition schools, but they sounded so boring. Ironically, someone in my office told me about Integrative Nutrition. I was intrigued, so I flew to New York from San Francisco for an orientation and thought it was amazing. I signed up right away.

If you light a lamp for somebody,
it will also brighten your path.

—*Buddhist saying*

CHAPTER 8:

COUNSELING CLIENTS

You are beginning to know what it feels like to be a Health Counselor. You are most likely discovering that health counseling is a highly rewarding undertaking and a lot more interesting than watching television or working at your computer.

The core of our work as Health Counselors is to support our clients on their journey to health and wellness. We are a source of loving encouragement, we share helpful tips and we help them move forward with their goals.

In your work with clients, you are going to have some who are gems and some who are more difficult. In this chapter we provide you with some ideas on how to work successfully with all your clients, and what to do if and when you have clients who are difficult or who have complex health concerns that demand the services of a medical professional.

TIPS FOR SUCCESSFUL CLIENT-COUNSELOR RELATIONSHIPS

INCREASE FOODS THAT SUPPORT HEALTH

If you can get your clients to eat more greens, vegetables, whole grains, sweet vegetables and healthy fats and proteins, you will dramatically change their lives. The food we eat makes our blood and our cells, and feeds our thoughts. By supporting your clients to increase healthy foods, they will see and feel the changes. Eventually, unhealthy foods will get crowded out, and your clients will be motivated to take their health to the next level.

REDUCE FOODS THAT DON'T SUPPORT HEALTH

As you know, most health conditions will improve with the reduction of meat, milk, sugar, caffeine and artificial/chemicalized junk food. Work slowly to add healthier options into your clients' diets, so that over time they can reduce foods that don't support health and energy.

START WITH SECONDARY FOOD, THEN INCORPORATE PRIMARY FOOD

Many Health Counselors have their food figured out. They know what works for them, and how to eat to get the most energy. Sometimes they automatically think everyone else has this figured out as well. These counselors often jump right into primary food issues with their clients, skipping over the incremental education around secondary food. This is not an effective strategy. If you want your clients to experience change and increased health, the best thing you can do is target their secondary food first. Have them incorporate more leafy greens, whole grains, high-quality protein and home-cooked food first. Once they have these foods as part of their regular diet, you can begin to look at the primary food issues that are out of balance and need change. Without first changing the food that people eat, it is difficult to change their lifestyle choices.

LOVE UP YOUR CLIENTS

Offer unending encouragement and support, and compliment them on their progress often. You may even want to send them a card or letter in the mail acknowledging how far they have come. Remember details about their lives, such as pets' and family members' names. Let them know you are happy to be working with them.

LISTEN

Provide your clients with a safe space to talk and be heard. When you are present with clients and actively listen, you will find that your intuition will guide you during your sessions. Oftentimes, the client just wants to talk. Remember, you don't have to solve their problems, but by simply having someone who listens, your client will figure out the answers to their issues.

DEFINE CLIENT GOALS

When you begin a health counseling program, it is important to have the client fill out the Welcome Handout, where they clearly define their goals for the program. Clients must first be aware of their present situation and define what they would like to accomplish. It is also valuable to continually check in with the client around their progress towards goals. You can create new goals or redefine existing goals as their program continues.

FOLLOW SESSION OUTLINES

We provide you with outlines for each of your sessions (1 through 12). You do not need to follow them word for word, but the outlines provide direction for you and the client. Review the outline for each client session before the session begins.

FOCUS ON THE POSITIVES

Always start your sessions by asking the client what is new and good. Often, people tend to focus only on what is not going well. As you help clients focus on what they are doing that is positive and what is good in their lives, they create a space for more good to enter.

HANDOUTS AND GIVEAWAYS

Provide the client with handouts and giveaways (food samples, CDs, books, self-care items) at each session. You will be given all of these handouts. Feel free to add your own touches.

TWO OR THREE RECOMMENDATIONS PER SESSION

End your sessions with two or three simple recommendations that the client can work on until you meet for your next session. Remember, it is important to not overwhelm the client with too much work, and you should always go at a pace that's comfortable for the client.

ASK QUESTIONS

Ask clients questions to get them thinking. You don't need to come up with all the answers to your clients' problems. They know more about their lives than you do. With the appropriate questions, they will figure out so much on their own. After you ask the question, give them time to respond and come up with their own conclusions. Here are some sample questions you might ask:

- "Why?"
- "What?"
- "How is that working for you?"
- "What do you think you should do?"
- "What do you think you should eat?"
- "Whom can you turn to for more support?"

Notes:

HELP YOUR CLIENT GET SUPPORT

Encourage your clients to get support outside of your sessions from family, friends, their community, spiritual groups and other groups that encourage connection and community.

PERSONALIZE THE PROGRAM

If you have expertise in other areas related to health, such as yoga, Pilates or massage, you can incorporate these into your program. Chances are, if there is something that you enjoy doing that has helped you with your own health and happiness, your clients could benefit from it as well. This could include things like meditation, art, music, writing or any other type of creative outlet. Add your personal touch and complement the program with topics specific to each client and their goals.

KEEP TRACK OF CLIENT PROGRESS

Keep track of your clients' progress between each session on the Client Progress Form that you are provided with. Remind your clients of what they are accomplishing while working with you.

RESPONSIBILITY

Let the clients take ownership of their health, have them commit and be willing to do the work.

CREATE A PARTNERSHIP

Clients are accustomed to relating to hired professionals as experts or authority figures. Collaboration works best when there are no traditional roles. Get out of the need to claim all the credit or have all the answers.

BE A COMPASSIONATE GUIDE

You don't need to tell your clients everything they should do. Ask them what they want you to do or not to do in the program. You are not healing them, they are healing themselves. Be honored to be a part of the process. You actually help the client more when you are less attached to getting results. When you are attached to outcome, you can get tense and stop breathing as deeply. Take deep breaths often during sessions to release attachment.

DEDICATION

Put your focus on the client, on what the client wants and on ways to help them achieve it. Be committed to clients' goals, outcomes, growth, learning, experimentation, integrity, discovery and evolution. Try offering new food options and new ideas, and help them make your suggestions a priority. Remind them that you will support them and hold them accountable, but they need to be motivated to do the work.

BE GENTLE BUT DEMANDING

Being too soft or nice will not help your clients. Not confronting an issue because it makes you uncomfortable is unfair to the client.

RESPECT DIFFERENCES

Remember, your client is not you. Meet your client where they are and do not impose your views on what is nutritionally right. You are probably highly advanced because you have been interested in nutrition for quite some time, but not everyone is as in tune with their diet as you are. Let the client set a pace that is comfortable for them. You can give them an extra push, but you want to set them up for success. Go slowly and give them recommendations you know they will follow.

COURTESY

Insist that you are both on time, prepared for sessions and show up feeling 100 percent. Have the client pay on time, don't reschedule appointments, clarify your rescheduling protocol for yourself and go over your policies with the client, especially if they miss or arrive late to a session.

CLIENT RETENTION

There are two aspects of client retention. One is keeping your clients satisfied with the six-month program, so they don't want to withdraw. The other is re-signing clients for another six months or a maintenance program when their first program is up.

It is important that each and every one of your clients is a raving fan of you and your program. They should be so thrilled about working with you that they tell everyone they know about you, and maybe even sign up for a second six-month program. And the happier your clients are with you, the more enjoyable it will be for you to work with them.

Notes:

 CLIENT RETENTION TIPS

1. RESPECT

Treat your clients the way you would want to be treated if you were spending money on your own health. What would that look like?

2. RELIABILITY

It's important to be on time, keep your appointments and fulfill your promises. They depend on you to be their support system, so if you promise to give a client further information about a particular topic, make it a priority and get it done. Support your clients on achieving the goals they set forth in the beginning of their program.

2. CONSTANT CONTACT

It is important to stay in touch with your clients, so they feel important You can have a special "client only" email list, where you send them bonus information, or other tidbits about health. Send clients' notes in the mail letting them know

how well they are doing. You may want to send them a card or call them on their birthday. What other special touches can you do to make people feel special?

2. FLEXIBILITY

Every client is unique, and they will want and need different things. You should be clear on each client's goals as you begin your work with them and your program to meet their needs. One client may be interested in learning about cooking at home for their family, while another client may not want to cook, but merely learn which foods to choose at a restaurant. Provide giveaways that relate to what you've talked about in your sessions. Make recommendations based on their individual circumstances.

The best way to create raving fans is to support your clients on achieving the goals they set forth in the beginning of their program. Be in constant communication about what their goals are and how you can support them to attain these aspirations. To keep your clients happy, it is extremely important that you maintain a high level of professionalism. You should be on time, prepared, stick to your word, send them notes after each session and reminders before each session. You do not want to let your clients down in any way. They depend on you to be their support system, and even if you are a day late in doing something that you promised (such as email an article or give them the address to a yoga studio), they may think that they were not a priority.

As we've mentioned, it is highly recommended to get the payment from your clients at the beginning of their program. Once the money is out of the way, in their minds it has already been paid for. If they have to write you a new check every month or pay you in cash every month, they may question the purchase each time. Finalizing payment up-front is important to retaining clients.

Make sure your clients feel that their program is individualized. Provide giveaways that relate to what you've talked about in your sessions. Make recommendations based on their individual circumstances. Send clients notes in the mail letting them know how well they are doing. You may also want to incorporate personalized welcome letters or birthday cards. When it is time to give them the giveaway at the end of each session, let them know how it will be helpful for them. Even if it's a tongue cleaner and they have not talked about their dental health, let them know that using a tongue cleaner is a great way to reduce cravings or increase the satisfaction of kissing. They will appreciate your thoughtfulness.

These extra touches do not take a lot of your time and will add tremendously to customer satisfaction. Take into account that the higher your customer's satisfaction is, the more enjoyable your job will be. If your clients are happy to see you, tell you about how much they love working with you and also spread the word to others, your confidence will increase, as will the size of your business and your personal fulfillment.

SAMPLE CLIENT SURVEY

Surveys are a great way to find how your client has enjoyed their experience with you. The answers will serve as feedback as you continue to improve the services in your six-month program. The following is a simple survey, you can send by email to any of your past or current clients. Once you have these answers, see what themes come up. You can use some of these responses to improve your marketing materials and sales conversations.

1. How did you first hear about me (Jane Smith Health Counseling)?

....

....

....

2. What were the initial reasons and specific concerns you had, as well as the benefits you were hoping to achieve in our program, before we actually began working together?

....

....

....

Notes:

3. How did you first hear about me (Jane Smith Health Counseling)?

....

....

....

4. What were the main benefits you received during your program?

....

....

....

5. How has your life improved because of this work?

....

....

....

6. What suggestions or recommendations do you have that could help me improve the quality of my programs?

....

....

....

7. Would you be willing to refer others to me, and if so why?

....

....

....

RE-SIGNING CLIENTS

As you come to the end of a six-month program, you can offer your client the opportunity to work with you for six more months. It's best to offer this to clients whom you truly enjoy working with and who you think would benefit from more of your support. It might feel scary to ask clients to keep seeing you, but you have nothing to lose. Simply let them know that you are interested and available for further support. Chances are, they are wondering how they are going to manage without seeing you anymore!

A second six-month program can be enormously significant for clients. They already have a trusting relationship with you, and they are healthier and are thinking more clearly than they were six months earlier. In their second program they are able to work very deeply on creating a life they love even more.

To re-sign clients, at the end of session 10 or 11, mention to them that you have a special offer for people who sign up a second time. Let them know they have come a long way through their work with you, and will continue to grow and thrive even more over the next six months. This gives them some time to think about what they want their life to look like after their program ends.

You can also offer them a maintenance program, seeing them once a month for six months or every other week for three months. A maintenance program is a lower cost, lower commitment arrangement can appeal to clients who crave more support but don't have the time or resources to do another six-month program. If your client is having difficulty deciding what's best for them, use your closing the deal skills to walk them through the process. If they decide to work with you again, have them re-sign the appropriate Program Agreement, get their payment, set up their new appointments and congratulate them on making such a powerful commitment to themselves and their health.

IDEAL CLIENTS

As we discussed in Chapter 4, in the beginning of your career as a Health Counselor, you will take on different types of clients—various ages, income levels, and genders. Working with a variety of people will help you discover which type of clients you enjoy most. It will soon become clear which clients energize and inspire you. It is these people whom you should declare your ideal clients and build your target market strategy around.

The clearer you are about the clients you want to work with, the easier it will be for you to find them and for them to find you. It is possible to have a thriving part-time or full-time practice working with clients whom you truly enjoy. You do not need to suffer working with clients who make your life miserable simply for the paycheck or for experience. We encourage you to only take on clients you find pleasure in working with.

MY IDEAL CLIENT

In order to attract your ideal client, first identify what that client would be like. Use the chart on the following page to get clear about the characteristics and personality traits

Notes:

that your client must have and preferably has. If you already have one ideal client, you can use that person's qualities as a guide.

Must Have	Preferably Has	Preferably Does Not Have	Must Not Have

Take a moment to look at your ideal client chart every day. As you become more mindful of exactly who you are looking for, you will notice that type of person showing up more frequently in your life.

DIFFICULT CLIENTS

Working with clients who are difficult will drain your energy and stifle the progress of your practice. Your program is an intimate relationship that is shared for six months. Being in that relationship with even one client who creates complications can ruin your exhilaration and motivation around being a Health Counselor.

Try to identify potentially difficult clients during the health history and do not sign them up for your program.

Type of clients you may not want to work with:

- People who don't show up or come late and make excuses. If they do this from the beginning, they will most likely continue through the entire program.

- People who complain over every detail of the program or the Program Agreement. An ideal client is ready and willing to sign up and enjoy your program, but a difficult client has many hesitations.

- People who challenge you and question your abilities. If someone isn't sure they want to work with you, it most likely means they will not be successful in your program.

- Individuals who try to negotiate fees. People who take an inch will often try to take a mile down the road.

- People who don't do the work, resist your guidance, make excuses or lie.

- Any people who, for whatever reason, get on your nerves and are difficult to be around. Some people will not be a good fit for you, so let them walk out the door and save yourself the agony.

If someone who fits this description comes to a health history, simply complete the Health History Form and thank them for coming. Escort them out without explaining your program or the fees. If they ask you about it, you can honestly say that you don't think the two of you would make a good fit, or that your program probably isn't best suited to fit their particular needs. You don't need to go into detail about why, just politely send them on their way. You could also refer them to someone else.

If you already have difficult clients, it is best to discontinue your work with them. You can explain to them that your skill set is not suited to match their specific needs. Let them know you can provide a referral to another practitioner who is better suited to help them reach their goals. You can refund their money, prorated for the number of months you worked together, or give them back their post-dated checks. Let them go, and focus your energy on getting more ideal clients.

PREVENTING NO-SHOWS

The absolute best way to prevent no-shows at scheduled sessions is to have your clients pay up-front and to be clear from the beginning about your tardiness and attendance policies. If you do not get paid, either in full with post-dated checks or with a credit card number up-front, you are sending a message to your clients that they do not have to be committed. Let them know that if they don't give you 24-hour notice for a cancellation they cannot make up the session.

You may also want to send out a reminder email or call the day before each session. Confirm the time and place of your appointment, and let them know that you look forward to seeing them.

WHEN A CLIENT WANTS TO WITHDRAW

There are a few reasons why clients may want to withdraw from your program. The most common grounds are fear, not achieving their expected results, thinking they already know everything and financial issues.

In most cases, this will happen halfway through your six-month program. If and when this happens, share with your client that this is common. Tell them that many people go through this at the halfway point. You can gently remind them that they signed a Program Agreement, which is legally binding. Remind them how far they have come. Explain why the program is six months long. Give them the space to express their concerns. Ask them if there is anything that they would like to see happen moving forward.

Notes:

You can mention a few things that you see them accomplishing over the next three months, and tell them you look forward to supporting them in making those changes. Most people who contemplate withdrawing from your program are asking for more support.

In special circumstances, you may want to let your client withdraw. If they lost their job and genuinely cannot afford it, if they were diagnosed with a serious illness or if they are extremely difficult clients, it may be in your best interest to discontinue the program and refund them the money for sessions that have not yet occurred. To prevent withdrawals, be in constant communication with your clients about their goals and what they are looking for from your work together.

FRAUD FACTOR

At this point some of you still might not be seeing clients. Maybe you aren't even telling people that you are a Health Counselor. For one reason or another you feel you are not equipped to counsel the public. Maybe you are waiting until you graduate, until you've read all the books and heard from all the guest speakers or until your own health is "perfect."

You are thinking, "Who am I to tell other people what to do around their health?"

You feel like a fraud when you label yourself a professional Health Counselor. We call this feeling the "Fraud Factor."

List all the reasons why you feel unequipped to counsel the public:

1. ....

2. ....

3. ....

4. ....

5. ....

6. ....

7. ....

8. ....

Where do these beliefs come from?

1. ....

2. ....

3. ....

4. ....

5. ....

How can you let go of these self-limitations and create new thought patterns centered on your incredible skills and intuition as a Health Counselor?

....

....

....

....

....

....

We are here to tell you that you are not a fraud. You already know more about health than most of the people on this planet. Your knowledge, along with the tools we teach you, is enough to help people increase their health and happiness. You do not need to be 100 percent healthy and perfect to be a Health Counselor. Listen, ask questions, give recommendations and use the resources you have available to you.

This is the time to start seeing clients! Identify what is keeping you from getting out there and sharing what you know and who you are. Is it your busy schedule? Or low self-esteem? Do you think you don't know enough about nutrition? Use your counselor and the school to help you overcome these obstacles. This is the year when you will have the most support. This is the year to begin. You have something very valuable to share with people, so get out there!

WORKING WITH CHILDREN

Working with young people can be extremely rewarding. Getting five-year-olds to eat kale on a regular basis is an incredible accomplishment because their lives will turn out completely differently than if they were just eating McDonald's and Doritos.

If you enjoy the company of children and you would like to incorporate them into your client base, go for it! You can work with them just as you would with any other client. You will be provided with a Child Health History Form.

Don't underestimate children. They are often more open to change and new foods than adults give them credit for. Because they have not been alive as long, children do not have as many habits built up as adults do. They are often more in touch with their bodies and surroundings than adults.

With the right support, they have strong instincts about how to get themselves well. Spend a good amount of time at the start of your program building rapport and connection. This is critical because it makes your child client feel safe enough to open up to you. Ask great questions, lead them gently and allow them to trust you. Be encouraging and show them you understand their situation. Treat them with respect and make them feel special and that you are truly listening.

Children are spontaneous. You may need to shorten your sessions or incorporate movement and stretch breaks to keep their attention and focus. You don't want their time with you to feel too serious.

Add fun to your sessions with children:

- Lead them on a kid-friendly health food store tour.
- Let them come up with their own recommendations.
- Make kid-friendly food together, such as ice pops or "ants on a log."
- Meet somewhere unexpected such as a playground or sit on pillows on your office floor.
- Bring in food, giveaways and other props for them to touch, look at, taste and discover.
- Give them stickers and different colored pens to use in their food journal and notebook.

Keep in mind that it takes children three tries to like a new food. The first time it is usually too new, the second time they still don't like it, but by the third try their taste buds usually come around. So be patient.

Depending on the age of your client, the parent will play a major role in the program. In some cases a parent may sit in on sessions. During the health history determine how involved the parents will be, and make sure everyone is on the same page. When working with children ages 12 and under, you will want the parents to be involved. Give parents all handouts so they understand the work their child is doing with you. It's also good if you provide the parents with recipes and bring them along on the health food store tour so they become aware of how to incorporate healthier foods into the household.

Some graduates who work with children have every other session with the parent and every other session with the child. This way they get to work with the parent around how to balance their life while raising a child. They teach the parent cooking techniques, and support the parent in being a healthy example. In the sessions with the child, the counselor introduces healthy snack foods and talks about the food-mood connection and primary food.

CHILDREN'S HEALTH HISTORY
PLEASE WRITE OR PRINT CLEARLY

Name: ....

Address: ....

Telephone: .... Email or parents' email: ....

Age: .... Birthday: .... Place of Birth: ....

Height: .... Weight: .... Grade: ....

Why did you come for this health history? ....

Do you enjoy school? Please explain: ....

Do you have a large or small group of friends? ....

Who is your best friend? ....

What do you do for fun? ....

What is your favorite sport or activity? ....

What are fun things you do with family? ....

What are your favorite things to do when you are alone? ....

What chores you do around the house? ....

When is bedtime? .... When do you wake up? ....

Do you ever wake up at night? .... Do you ever have nightmares? ....

Do you get bellyaches? .... Do you get headaches or earaches? ....

Is it hard to see or read? .... Do you get itchy? ....

Do you have allergies or sensitivities? ....

Does anything else hurt? ....

What do you eat for breakfast? ....

What do you eat for lunch? ....

What do you eat for dinner? ....

What do you eat for snacks? ....

What do you drink? ....

What foods do you wish you could eat more often? ....

What food do you wish you never had to eat again? ....

What do you want to learn about your body and about food? ....

TEENAGE CLIENTS

Teenagers usually respond very well to working with Health Counselors. Most seek adults whom they can confide in and look up to. If you are interested in working with teenagers, you can begin by offering workshops at high schools and teen camps. If your goal is to sign up clients for a six-month program, we recommend you invite the parents to the workshops as well because they are the ones who are going to pay for and probably drive the teenager to see you. You want to show the parents your professionalism and the potential health benefits for their child. Having parental support and encouragement will greatly increase your teen clients' satisfaction and success in your program.

Teens react well to being granted greater responsibility and being treated like adults, so the parents of your teenage clients don't need to be closely involved in the six-month program. When signing the Program Agreement, make it clear that your sessions will be between you and the teenager only. You can invite the parent to attend the monthly seminars as a guest of your teenage client.

If the teenager shares information with you that could affect their safety or others, it is imperative that you support your client by telling their parents. Examples of this are drug use, suicidal comments, violent tendencies and eating disorders. If your client refuses to tell their parents, you must tell them yourself. Telling parents the truth will help your clients overcome their struggles.

HEALTH COUNSELING PARAMETERS

Health Counselors do not heal anyone. Clients do the work and are responsible for their own life and health. We are their "guide on the side."

It is important not to work with clients who have major health concerns or who are taking multiple prescription drugs. Their concerns are often too complex and are best supported through other means.

When working with clients who have minor health concerns, use the reference guides we gave you to look up their ailments. *The Complete Guide to Nutritional Healing* and *Healing with Whole Foods* are two excellent sources of information. You can look up conditions from migraine headaches to acid reflux, from dandruff to candida. These books will give dietary suggestions to help people overcome certain health concerns. You can share these tools with your clients by showing them information in the book and discussing this together. Also, if you have clients who take one or two medications, use the Physicians Desk Reference (PDR) to investigate possible side effects and contra-indications (food or otherwise) associated with medications.

You should never tell a client to stop taking medications, or to stop seeing their doctor or psychiatrist. Nor should you ever encourage clients to make radical life changes (quitting a job, leaving a relationship, moving out of town). Clients will come up with their own solutions to their problems, and when they do you can support them with the decisions they make.

The client is in charge of their life, and they are ultimately responsible for the outcomes of their decisions. In order to protect yourself against any possible liability, be sure to always have your clients fill out the Program Agreement and explain to them that they are responsible for their own decisions.

WHEN TO REFER CLIENTS

As a new Health Counselor, you should seek out clients who are in good overall health. Clients should not be on multiple medications. They should not have seriously advanced, chronic, critical or complex health conditions, such as cancer, degenerative illnesses or life-threatening eating disorders. It is fine to work with people who have autoimmune disorders like diabetes, thyroid issues and metabolic syndromes. In these cases it is also important that the client be under the care of a medical practitioner. We recommend the client alert their practitioner that they are in your program. This way, you can help support the efforts and recommendations of the medical care provider.

If you are unsure about working with any particular client, you should seek the advice of your counselor or a trusted healthcare professional, and err on the side of caution. Sometimes clients may not reveal this information until they are already into the program with you. In this case it is imperative that the clients already be working with a healthcare professional and that the professional knows the client is working with you.

If the client has cancer, a life-threatening illness or a serious chronic condition and refuses to work with a medical care professional, we strongly urge you to stop working with that client to protect both parties involved. You can refer these clients to a medical doctor, osteopath, naturopath or nurse practitioner. Health counseling is not a substitute for seeing a medical professional.

It is helpful for beginning Health Counselors to keep certain distinctions in mind in order to determine whether a client needs additional support from a mental health professional. Developing active listening is the best way to be aware of whether or not you should refer your client to another professional to check for underlying complex medical or emotional issues.

Listen to your intuition. If you think you might be in over your head, you most likely are. Set and trust your boundaries. Don't let your desire to be helpful or your fears of rejecting someone allow you to be drawn into an inappropriate situation. Depending on the extent of your client's condition, you may still be able to work with the client while they are seeking medical or mental health treatment.

If your client shows signs of depression, mania, mental instability or suicidal tendencies, you should refer them immediately to a mental health professional.

Signs of depression:

- Decreased energy, fatigue
- Feelings of hopelessness, pessimism
- Persistent sad, anxious or "empty" mood
- Feelings of guilt, worthlessness, helplessness
- Thoughts of death or suicide, suicide attempts
- Appetite and/or weight loss, overeating, weight gain
- Insomnia, early morning awakening or oversleeping
- Difficulty concentrating, remembering, making decisions
- Loss of interest in pleasure or hobbies that were once enjoyable, including sex

Signs of mania:

- Poor judgment
- Racing thoughts
- Increased talking
- Suicidal thoughts
- Grandiose notions
- Unusual irritability
- Increased sexual desire
- Decreased need for sleep
- Markedly increased energy
- Inappropriate social behavior
- Abnormal or excessive elation

Signs of mental instability:

- Is the client out of touch with reality, fixated on events of the past?
- Are they emotionally unable to cope or to follow through on basic strategies, excessively anxious, emotional or angry?
- Do they suffer from the result of a recent trauma, domestic violence or grief/loss?
- Is there a substance abuse issue or other serious addiction?
- A client's reference to suicidal thoughts or tendencies should be taken very seriously. Handle them in the following ways:
  - When talking about thoughts of suicide with a client, do not swear to secrecy.
  - Ask the client if they are currently having thoughts of suicide or have a suicide plan. Be aware that the more detailed the plan and the greater the access to the means to carry out the plan, the greater the risk of suicide.

- Ask them if they are working with a mental health professional. If they are not, have them contact their doctor or the suicide hotline in your area to get a referral. They can also go to the local hospital.
- Have them make a plan to meet with someone either on the spot or within the next few hours. If there will be an interval of time before they will be meeting with the person, ask them to agree with you to not take any actions to hurt themselves at least until they meet with the professional. Help them to identify and call a support person that can come and be with them until their appointment in order to help them stay safe and reduce feelings of isolation.
- If the client is a minor, talk to their parent or guardian about how to keep the client safe.
- Remind parents that if alcohol or drug use is involved, suicide risk is increased.

Whom to refer depressed and suicidal clients to:

- Doctor
- Therapist
- Psychiatrist
- Psychologist
- Rehab program
- Licensed social worker
- Mental health counselor

Making a professional link with a mental health professional is a good idea. You can refer clients to them if need be, and they can act as a resource on matters related to mental health.

ADDITIONAL ISSUES TO CONSIDER FOR REFERRALS

Child abuse and maltreatment is defined as:

- Sexual abuse
- Malnourishment
- Use of drugs or alcohol
- Extreme emotional abuse
- Improper/inadequate supervision
- Substantial risk for physical injury
- Physical abuse, injury or excessive corporal punishment
- Inadequate shelter, clothing, education, medical or surgical care

In the event that you witness or it is revealed to you that a minor is being abused or neglected in some way, we advise that a report be made to the child welfare agency or hotline in your area. The reporting phone number is usually listed in the front of your phone book or under your local department of social services.

If it is an emergency situation, the police should be called. If the person who revealed the instance of child abuse to you is the direct witness, encourage the witness to call and make a report. However, if you believe a child is truly in danger, we suggest you make the call. If you are not in a profession in which you are legally mandated to report these issues, you may do so anonymously.

If a client reveals that they were the victim of a relatively recent crime, such as rape or domestic violence, encourage them to report the incident to the local police department. In addition, the client should be encouraged to meet with a therapist or visit an intervention agency that deals with the post-traumatic issues of such events. The above is also relevant in cases where the incident occurred in the not-so-recent past. If a client still feels threatened by the perpetrator of a past crime, they should be encouraged to seek legal support or work with an appropriate intervention agency.

GRADUATE PROFILE

KELLEY DOBBINS, RN CCRN
Watertown, CT
kelsice@aol.com
2005 Graduate

When I started classes at Integrative Nutrition, I did not intend to start a business. I planned to use this education in the doctors' office where I work as a cardiac nurse. But when a coworker found out what I was doing, she asked me if I would work with her. Before I knew it, I was graduating with 10 clients and my own part-time business.

Before coming to the school, I lived my life in search of losing the last 10 pounds. As a marathon runner and figure skater prone to high cholesterol, I could never find any dietary advice that fit with my athletic training. While attending the school, I figured out exactly how to eat for my body and lifestyle. Now I don't care what my weight is because I feel so good.

In my business, I have three different target markets: health professionals, people with high cholesterol and athletes. I work with stressed-out healthcare workers because I was one of them before coming to Integrative Nutrition. I was a burnt out, frustrated nurse, and now I am a healthy, happy Health Counselor and look forward to the work I do every day. I help my colleagues in healthcare understand that they need to prioritize their own health and well-being so they can be in a better position to take care of others. This is something that we never learned in nursing school, and I believe it is one of the main reasons for the nursing shortage today.

In addition to my private clients, I work with patients in the doctors' office to reduce their dependency on drugs for lowering their cholesterol levels. I also enjoy working with athletes to increase their performance through nutrition and creative visualization. I teach them to enjoy their training and development as much as the ultimate outcome, a pivotal shift I made during my year in school.

> "I now know whatever my dream, I can make it happen."

Becoming a Health Counselor has changed my life. Before Integrative Nutrition, I was always invisible and afraid of failure. I never wanted to make a mistake, and now I embrace mistakes as a way to learn. I now know whatever my dream, I can make it happen. Working with clients to give them the tools to make healthy food choices, not obsess over what they eat, and take good care of themselves is the best job in the world.

In nursing there is no time to listen, but in health counseling I know the best tool I have is my listening skills. Nurses are taught to stay quiet in the background. We let the doctors do the talking and make important decisions. This completely changed for me while in school. I learned to speak up, find my voice and recognize that what I have to say is incredibly valuable. I never thought I'd have my own business and speak in front of groups. I am even writing a book with one of the doctors on cholesterol management, something that I would not have been able to do without the confidence I developed while at the school. If I can do this, anyone can!

You can't just sit there and wait for people to give you that golden dream; you've got to get out there and make it happen for yourself.

—Diana Ross

CHAPTER 9:

MAINTAINING MOMENTUM
AND STAYING BALANCED

It takes a few years to build a solid business. Don't expect it all to happen overnight. It may seem to you that some of your classmates or our alumni had clients fall into their laps. This is not the case. This takes focus, sticking with it, and putting your energy into your business. If you are consistently putting yourself out there and building your visibility in your community and within your target market, you will succeed. Please remember to focus on what is working; put your energy and effort into solutions and methods to grow your practice. Don't focus on mistakes, but rather learn from them, as those are really lessons that will guide you to do even better as you move forward.

Everyone has times when they doubt their ability to do this work. It is the nature of being in business for yourself. What's important is that you push yourself through those times and continue moving forward. You will need self-motivation to stay inspired by what you do and have your goals in sight. Keep reminding yourself why you wanted to be a Health Counselor in the first place. Take constant inventory of the positive influences you are having on your clients, family and friends. You are a source of inspiration for your community, and you have so much to offer!

STARTING WHERE YOU ARE

Whether you have zero or 30 clients, accept where you are and move from there. You do not want to be ahead of yourself or behind yourself in any way. For example, if you haven't signed any clients yet, you don't want to focus on building a website or writing a book. Instead, focus your effort on getting health histories. Likewise, if you already have a full practice and can't handle any more clients, you don't need to spend hours booking a workshop; your energy is probably better spent on time management and deepening your counseling skills.

Here are some recommended action steps to take, depending on where you are in your business:

IF YOU ARE STILL LOOKING FOR CLIENTS

This is a great place to be because your business can only get better from here. You are at the beginning of creating a career you love, and you have so much to look forward to. Your task now is to fill your pipeline with potential clients by networking in person. Tell people you are a Health Counselor. Network at business groups and parties. Give talks. Invite people to health histories and do as many as you can. The more health histories you do, the sooner you will have paying clients. Figure out who you know is connected to your target market. Build those relationships so that you have a consistent stream of people who send you clients.

IF YOU ARE COUNSELING PART-TIME

Continue to focus on marketing yourself in person. Stay visible and in demand so that there is always someone about to sign up with you. This way, when a client finishes a program, you can enroll a new client to fill that slot right away. Give talks, network and make special offers to clients who refer people that sign up with you.

Evaluate how many clients are ideal for you. Are you happy counseling part time? Do you want to eventually go full-time? If so, when? Some people are happy counseling only five clients at a time. Others want to counsel 10, 20 or 30 clients. Some new counselors think that if their number of clients plateaus along the way they can't do this work full-time. This isn't true. You can grow your business if you want to. Decide for yourself how many clients are ideal, then increase or decrease your marketing hours, or change your action steps to get the number you want.

IF YOU ARE COUNSELING FULL-TIME

At this point you have completed a lot of the basic marketing work it takes to attract clients. You are probably managing a lot of paperwork, people and opportunities. The time you spend on marketing should be limited and focused. Do one powerful marketing activity each day. Or set aside one day a week for marketing and take seven actions.

Put energy into building a sustainable business structure. Manage your time well and increase your level of self-care so you don't burn out. Hire an assistant at $10 to $15 an hour to help you with administrative details. Enlist PR or media relations help so you can get your business out there without having to do all the footwork yourself.

You can also take advantage of passive marketing techniques, where other people find clients for you. Build referral networks with other practitioners so they send potential clients your way. Underpromise and overdeliver for all your clients, so that they become raving fans and spread the word about how fabulous you are.

In Chapter 1 we asked you to set goals for what you want your health counseling business to look like.

Have you achieved them? ....

If so, what led to your success? ....

How do you feel? ....

If not, that's okay too. Take an honest look at why not.

What is one obstacle you are committed to overcoming? ....

Have your goals changed, and if so, how? ....

What can you do differently in the future to meet your goals? ....

HAVING FUN

If you want your career as a Health Counselor to be satisfying, you must find a way to incorporate having fun into your business. Being an overly serious workaholic who is adamantly attached to changing the world will get old soon enough. Take a step back, enjoy your precious life and find a way to create balance between work and play.

Notice what parts of health counseling bring you the most energy and excitement. Do you absolutely love giving talks? Sending out your newsletter? Leading health food store tours? Whatever you enjoy most, do more of it. Similarly, notice what parts of health counseling drain your energy and do less of those!

What are three parts of health counseling that drain your energy?

1. ....

2. ....

3. ....

What are three parts of health counseling that turn you on?

1. ....

2. ....

3. ....

Notes:

How can you do less of things that drain your energy and more of what you truly enjoy?

1. ....

2. ....

3. ....

4. ....

5. ....

6. ....

SUPPORT PEOPLE

A happy and energized Health Counselor is one who is getting support. The only way to get the support you need is to ask for it. You can't do everything alone, and by asking for assistance, in both your business and your personal life, your chances of success skyrocket.

Health counseling is a giving profession, meaning you are constantly giving to your clients, prospective clients and probably the majority of the people in your life. To ensure that there is a balance of give and take, you need to create a support structure or system that works for you, a way to recharge your battery and discharge stress. An ideal support structure is made up of everyone in your life. You can never have too much encouragement. And know that it is possible to have everyone in your life be supportive of who you are and what you are doing. It is a sign of strength to allow others to hold you up, to be vulnerable at times and to take into account the ideas of others.

IDEAS FOR FUN IN YOUR PRACTICE

- Create arts and crafts projects to do in your client sessions or in your seminars, such as collages, finger painting, candle making, painting pottery or making your own holiday cards.
- Instead of a monthly seminar, take clients out dancing, to karaoke or for a picnic.
- Hold client sessions outside somewhere beautiful.
- Invite exciting guest speakers to your monthly seminars, such as belly dancers, palm readers, fashion experts, feng shui practitioners or creative writing teachers.
- Offer to help your clients de-clutter their home or kitchen. Hold a session at their place and give them tips on how to clean up clutter.
- Make it a goal to laugh at least once in each session. If this is difficult for you, find something that makes you laugh and keep it in your office at all times.

List five people in your life and how they support you.

1. ....

....

2. ....

....

3. ....

....

4. ....

....

5. ....

....

Find a way to appreciate these people for all they do. Tell them how grateful you are for having them in your life. Explain what they do that you find helpful, and encourage them to keep on doing it! Find ways to make these people more central in your life. And make sure it is a mutually supportive relationship, where both people benefit.

Now, ask yourself how you might be able to get this kind of support from others. Are there people in your life who you would like to be closer with, but whom you find unsupportive? How can you ask them for the kind of support you need? Or is it time to reduce their role in your life or cut them out? If it is family members who are unsupportive, it is usually best to do whatever is in your power to be on good terms with them, without compromising yourself.

List five people who are unsupportive of you and how.

1. ....

....

2. ....

....

3. ....

....

4. ....

....

5. ....

....

Without a doubt, you are going to come across some people who are unsupportive of your decisions. These people may truly care about you and only want the best for you. If that is the case, communicate with them openly about why you are making the choices you are, and why you really need their support right now. Hear out their concerns, and reply honestly.

It is possible that these unsupportive people may not be the best people for you to have in your life anymore. There are those in this world who are very jealous, who don't want to see their friends doing well. There are also those who are scared of change and prefer everything to stay the same. If you are changing—beginning a new career, eating new foods and making different lifestyle choices—you will be challenging their reality. Ask yourself if there are some people whom you know in your heart you would be better off without. It is okay to let them go. You are not doing them, or yourself, any favors by continuing to be a part of a dysfunctional relationship. If breaking off contact seems drastic, you can downgrade your relationship, see them less often and give them less of your energy.

YOUR BUDDY

The people closest to you may not always be the best support people for your business. As much as they love you, their tolerance for hearing about another Sugar Blues talk or health history might be low. Your buddy from class is a valuable support person for you because they know where you are coming from, and they are also just starting out as a Health Counselor. The two of you should meet or speak regularly. Your buddy's duty is to listen to you, celebrate with you, commiserate with you, be your brainstorming partner and keep you focused on achieving your goals. This is also your duty to your buddy.

CREATING COMMUNITY

An important ingredient to the success of our school is community. As you know by now, many of our students make some of the best friends of their lives while they are here. This happens naturally because the school attracts people who are healthy, happy and who want to do something that inspires them and helps others. We strongly encourage you to take advantage of the community you have here at the school. Meet new people at each class weekend, have lunch with other students, get together outside of class and build relationships. Having other Health Counselors in your life is priceless. They know how to listen and give good advice and also can support you in your career.

LOCAL STUDY CHAPTERS

Integrative Nutrition has created local study chapters because we noticed that students truly enjoyed hanging out, getting to know and supporting one another. We highly encourage you to take advantage of this valuable resource. Attend local study chapters held by people in your area, or on the phone. Even better, hold your own local study chapter. Pick a topic related to business and invite as many people as you'd like. During the local study chapter, share business tips, stories, challenges and laughs.

BOARD OF DIRECTORS

A key to success is getting expert advice from supportive people who have more knowledge and experience than you. Corporations, schools and nonprofit foundations accomplish this by having boards of directors who advise them on their business decisions and goal planning. We recommend you create a board of directors for your health counseling business. Your board will share their knowledge, help you make important decisions, give you support, hold you accountable and help you reach new levels of success.

HOW TO CREATE A BOARD OF DIRECTORS

1. Decide whom to invite. You will need between four and six people on your board. Who are your peers and mentors with valuable insight to share? Do you know any accountants, lawyers or business professionals? A friend who works in marketing? A successful Health Counselor? Another experienced person in a healing profession?

2. Invite each person to participate in your business as an advisor. Share with them how committed you are to your business success and how much you value their wisdom and support.

3. Let each person know up front what their time commitment will be: one conference call each month for 30 to 60 minutes. Ask them what are three possible days and times they could meet every month (e.g., every third Tuesday at 5 p.m.). Choose a schedule that works for everyone.

4. Send an email to your entire group, introducing everyone to each other and asking them to mark the meeting schedule on their calendars. It should be the same week, day and time every month.

5. Use freeconference.com to schedule the calls. Be sure to send your board the phone number and any necessary access codes.

6. Before each call, choose two or three areas of your business where you need the most support.

    You could also prepare a summary of your business before each meeting to keep your board up to date on your progress. Make sure you leave time for group brainstorming.

7. Keep meetings regular because the consistent support is crucial to your success. If members need to leave your group, find others to replace them.

8. Appreciate your board and let them know how much you value their support. Send thank you cards, emails or small gifts.

9. Give back. Offer to be on their boards of directors in return.

Write down the names of five people you want on your board of directors.

1. ....

2. ....

3. ....

4. ....

5. ....

Your board does not have to be arranged in any formal way. The goal is to have regular contact with knowledgeable people who actively support you and your business growth. Set this up however works best for you.

HIRING A BUSINESS COACH

If you are clear that you want your business to grow, but you need more guidance on how to make that happen, you might want to hire a business coach. When your sessions end with your Health Counselor in the summer, your counselor may offer their services to you at a discounted rate. You may choose to take them up on this offer.

A different option would be to hire another Health Counselor as your coach. We have graduates who have been practicing successfully for years and offer business coaching to current students and alumni. Most of these people have probably already come and spoken during class. Their contact information is on the OEF and they would be delighted to hear from you and tell you about the business coaching that they offer.

MENTORS

Anyone who has ever had a mentor or been a mentor knows that the mentor-mentee relationship is beautiful. To guide a person through something that you have already experienced, to encourage them, warn them of the roadblocks and tell them they can do it, is an extremely rewarding experience. Likewise, having someone show you the ropes, someone you can confide in and trust, is priceless. Know that there are many people in the Integrative Nutrition community and in the world who would be honored to offer their expertise to you. Your Health Counselor is one of these people.

Ask yourself if you know someone whose business expertise you admire. Who is someone you aspire to be like? Pick up the phone or turn on your computer, and reach out to this person. Invite them to lunch, let them know that you've just started a new business and you'd love to share some ideas—that you really value their expert opinion.

List three people who you would like to have as your mentor.

1. ....

2. ....

3. ....

Now devise a plan for making them a part of your life. It might be appropriate to hire this person—if they are a business coach—or maybe you simply work towards building a friendly relationship. Know that you become like the people whom you associate with, so surrounding yourself with accomplished, first-rate people is a sure way to invite success.

SELF-CARE

A common vice among Health Counselors is that we can put too much energy into taking care of others we forget or don't have time to take care of ourselves. If you keep up this behavior, you will eventually burn out and have nothing to give anyone. You'll wonder where you went wrong; you may even develop an illness.

Your body sends you messages through its ailments to take better care of it. As a Health Counselor and a human being you must learn to discipline yourself to take care of your mental, physical, emotional and spiritual health.

Take note of the signs your body sends you when you are out of balance, burning the candle at both ends or not taking good enough care of yourself.

Notes:

List the top five ways here:

1. ....

2. ....

3. ....

4. ....

5. ....

Be on alert for these messages. Lovingly listen to them and take the appropriate action to get back into balance.

We encourage you to practice extreme self-care. What do we mean by extreme self-care? At least once a day do something to energize or rejuvenate yourself. This will look different for everyone, and it will look different depending on the day. It may mean getting a massage, going into nature, taking a bubble bath, cooking your favorite meal, going for a walk around the block at work, seeing a movie or whatever pleases you. It may be that you need to do two things a day for yourself, or even three. Hopefully, over time, self-care will become second nature to you, and you won't even consider putting everyone else's needs in front of your own.

STRESS

Stress has extremely negative effects on our overall health; it causes all sorts of illness, affects sleep and digestion, can lead to depression and lowers the quality of life. Develop reliable and simple ways to reduce stress. Experiment with meditation, hot towel scrubs, drinking more water, herbal tea, running outside or whatever helps you to quiet your mind and feel at peace. Eating well and doing regular physical activity are excellent ways to reduce stress and nurture yourself. Do whatever you need to make these things regular occurrences in your life.

What are the main sources of stress in your life at the moment?

1. ....

2. ....

3. ....

4. ....

5. ....

What are two steps you can take to let go of each stressors, or reduce or eliminate the stress they bring into your life?

Notes:

First Stressor ....

1. ....

2. ....

Second Stressor ....

1. ....

2. ....

Third Stressor ....

1. ....

2. ....

Fourth Stressor ....

1. ....

2. ....

Fifth Stressor ....

1. ....

2. ....

What are three things you know you can do that help you when you feel stressed?

1. ....

2. ....

3. ....

BE YOUR OWN BEST MANAGER

- Identify your values and operate from them.
- Clarify your purpose, priorities and goals.
- Design and implement an effective business plan.
- Create strategic plans of action.
- Learn to work smarter—not harder.
- Eliminate time wasters.
- Plan your days.
- Set a schedule and keep it.
- Take a stretch break every 20 minutes.

Notes:

- Be dressed for "work."
- Get feedback from colleagues and experts.
- Collect information: quotes, articles, statistics.
- Keep your workspace organized.
- Enhance telephone skills.
- Follow through with clients.
- Market your business consistently.
- Join at least one professional association.
- Develop powerful networking abilities.
- Keep accurate records.
- Be a calculated risk taker.
- Be willing to move on.
- Make sure your needs are being met.
- Exercise regularly.
- Create a support system.
- Continue your education.
- Get out of the house/office EVERY DAY!!!
- Take responsibility for yourself.
- Choose appropriate advisors.
- Keep things in perspective.
- Delegate the tasks you hate.
- Respect your mind's and body's cycles.
- Balance your personal and professional life.
- Remember, we're all human—we all make mistakes.
- Acknowledge your accomplishments every day.

Excerpted from *Business Mastery: A Guide for Creating a Fulfilling, Thriving Business and Keeping It Successful* by Cherie M. Sohnen-Moe, Sohnen-Moe Associates, Inc, $24.95.

TIME MANAGEMENT

Time management is an important skill to have in life, and it is especially critical when you own and operate your own business. Everyone has a different idea of time management. Whatever way you choose to look at it, we all have the same 24 hours in a day. The secret to managing your time effectively is to know how much it is worth and put your time toward the things that are most important to you.

What are your current beliefs about time? Not enough time in a day? Time goes by too quickly?

....

....

....

Notes:

What were your parents' beliefs and relationships to time?

....

....

....

....

....

....

....

Where does the majority of your time go?

....

....

....

....

....

....

....

What are three things you spend time on that aren't important to you?

1. ....

2. ....

3. ....

If you had more time, what would you do with it?

....

....

....

....

....

Notes:

How can you create more time to focus on what is really important to you?

....

....

....

....

....

....

To be good at time management does not mean that you have to work longer hours; you simply have to work smarter. Most people spend a good portion of their time on things that aren't effective. You want to maximize your working hours. Use the time you spend working wisely, so that you have more time to enjoy life, relax, have fun, cook, exercise and do whatever else you love.

TIPS FOR TIME MANAGEMENT

- Know how many hours you want to work each week.
- Identify the times of day when you do your best work.
- Note the times of day that are difficult for you to work.
- Build your schedule around your personal time cycles: when you work best, when it is best for you to exercise, to eat, to sleep, etc.
- Know your limit. How many hours a day and a week can you work before burning out?
- Acknowledge that there is a time in a day, after working a certain number of hours, when your efforts actually stop being useful.
- Clarify your goals and priorities, and make sure you spend most of your time working towards your biggest goals.
- Identify things you do that do not support your goals, and drop them.
- Make it your job to master the art of being successful in health counseling and staying balanced.

WEEKLY TIMESHEET

When you begin your practice, plan to spend about 75 percent of your time scheduling and doing health history consultations. The remaining 25 percent of your time will be spent following up with potential clients, keeping track of them and preparing for your meetings. Once you start signing clients, you'll probably spend about 50 percent of your time marketing your services and doing health histories, 30 percent of your time meeting with clients, and 20 percent of your time on follow-up and preparation.

WEEKLY TIMESHEET

	Health Histories	Client Sessions	Writing/ Newsletter	Marketing & Networking	Paperwork/ Phone	Email/Phone	Other
Monday a.m.							
Monday p.m.							
Tuesday a.m.							
Tuesday p.m.							
Wednesday a.m.							
Wednesday p.m.							
Thursday a.m.							
Thursday p.m.							
Friday a.m.							
Friday p.m.							
Saturday							
Sunday							

To help you master time management, we've created this weekly timesheet. Keep it, or one like it, in your office or in a journal. Before lunch each day, write in how many hours you spend on each category. Do the same again at the end of your workday. It's a good way to see where you are putting your energy and how long certain tasks take you. You may think that most of your time goes into marketing, but in actuality you may be spending hours upon hours on the internet. At the end of each week, review this time sheet, making note of where most of your time went. Reflect on it, and decide whether this was an effective use of your time. Make the appropriate adjustments in the following week.

BIG ROCKS

Named after a demonstration performed by a time-management expert, Franklin Covey, Big Rocks is a concept used throughout Integrative Nutrition. In the demonstration, the expert takes a jar and fills it with some big rocks. He asks his students if the jar is full. They say it is. He proceeds to dump gravel into the jar, and shake the jar around so the pieces of gravel fill up the spaces between the big rocks. He asks his students if the jar is full. They respond, "Probably not." Next, he pours sand into the jar, which fills in all the empty spaces between the gravel and the rocks. Again, he asks, "Is the jar full?" The students shout, "No!" Finally, he takes a pitcher of water and pours it into the jar until it is full to the brim. His point is not that you can always fit more into your jar, but that if you don't put in your big rocks first, you'll never get them in at all.

Each Monday morning, everyone on the Integrative Nutrition staff completes their Big Rocks list. This is an inventory of all the important tasks they are going to accomplish in the coming week, along with how many hours they plan to spend on each one. They list the tasks that take the most amount of time at the top. The reason we do this is not only so our supervisors know everything we are working on, but also to help us clarify for ourselves our work for the week. Some weeks we have too many hours, so we have to reevaluate our priorities, while other weeks we have extra time to work on upcoming or new projects.

Decide how many hours you would like to put toward health counseling this week and make a list of everything you would like to get done, both big and little. Make sure to add in time for phone calls, emails and other miscellaneous tasks. Now identify the Big Rocks. What are the items on this list that you absolutely must accomplish this week? And, honestly, how long is it going to take you to make them happen? Be realistic in terms of your time when doing your Big Rocks. Notice whether you have a tendency to underestimate or overestimate the amount of time it takes you to do things, and adjust your Big Rocks so that it is an accurate representation of the actual time spent on different projects.

Divide all the work you do into categories, such as "Counseling and Preparation," "Marketing," "Organization" and "Other." Then list the various projects within each category. For each category, note the number of hours you plan to spend on this work. You may want to chunk the time down, and list the amount of hours per project.

Doing your Big Rocks every Monday will keep you focused on the important things, and ideally prevent you from spending all your time on the little rocks, or things that don't really matter to you. If you do this each week, realistically representing your time, you will be saved from beating yourself up at the end of the week because you didn't get to the million other things on your list.

Keep your Big Rocks someplace visible and cross off your tasks as you accomplish them. The next week, list your top five accomplishments at the top of your new Big Rocks to remind yourself how well you are doing. The more you focus on your Big Rocks, and not the little pebbles, the more productive you will be. The first time you compile your Big Rocks it may take a little while, but after a few weeks, you'll breeze through it in about 20 minutes.

URGENT VS. IMPORTANT

This exercise is another effective tool to explore where your time goes. There are four quadrants here: important and urgent, not important and urgent, not urgent and important, and not urgent and not important. Everything you do in your life fits into

SAMPLE BIG ROCKS

JUNE 26-JUNE 30 BIG ROCKS
TOTAL HOURS = 40 HOURS

ACCOMPLISHMENTS		
		Signed 1 new client
		Attended BNI meeting
		Wrote July newsletter
		Booked a talk for September
		Cleaned office space

COUNSELING & PREPARATION		
18 hours	8	Client sessions
	4	July cooking class
	2	Prepare for client sessions: review notes, prepare handouts and giveaways
	2	Stock up on giveaways (books, cds, teas, etc.)
	2	Health histories

MARKETING		
7 hours	2	Lead workshop at community center
	2	Prepare for workshop: outline, handouts, etc
	1	Print flyers for workshop
	1	Contact newspaper about writing an article on summer foods
		Attend weekly BNI meeting

ORGANIZATION		
5 hours		File on receipts for tax purposes
		Update client folders: giveaway checklist and client progress
		Print Health History Forms
		Create extra new client folders
		Review finances and budget
		Follow up with all new contacts

MISCELLANEOUS		
5 hours		Phone
		Email
		Travel time

TO DO LATER THIS SUMMER		
		Workshop at teen camp in August
		Send press kit to local radio stations
		Drop in at new spa and talk to manager
		Send thank you letters to referral partners
		Seek out a new chiropractor to be a referral partner
		Attend weekly BNI meetings
		Take vacation

Notes:

one of these quadrants. Please fill in each quadrant with your regular activities that fit each category.

In which quadrant does most of your time go? Quite frequently, people spend the majority of their time doing things that they categorize as being urgent, but not important, and consequently things that are important get pushed aside. Use this exercise as motivation to cut out anything in your life that is not urgent and not important. Also, cut down the amount of time you spend on things that are urgent, but not important. Put the excess time and energy into things that are important to you, but not urgent.

FURTHERING YOUR EDUCATION

As a student at Integrative Nutrition, you already know enough to be a Health Counselor and to have a positive effect on anyone who comes your way. You do not need to know every little detail about nutrition and health in order to help your clients. With that said, furthering your education beyond what you learn with us can be exciting and energizing. Through reading books and attending classes, workshops or retreats on topics related to health, you can re-inspire yourself about your career.

URGENT VS. IMPORTANT

	IMPORTANT	NOT IMPORTANT
URGENT		
NOT URGENT		

Excerpted from *The 7 Habits of Highly Effective People: Powerful Lessons in Personal Change* by Stephen R. Covey, Fireside, $15.

Make a list of topics that are related to your work as a Health Counselor and that you would like to learn more about:

1. ....

2. ....

3. ....

4. ....

5. ....

How much money can you allocate in the next six months towards furthering your education? Even if you have $0, you can still learn almost anything. You can barter with a teacher, attend free seminars or borrow books from the library. The Open Center in New York City, Omega Institute in Rhinebeck, New York and Esalen and Heartwood in California all offer weekend, weeklong and month-long classes on topics related to health and wellness. Check them out, along with any other resources in your area.

What are some classes, workshops or books that are within your budget and related to your areas of interest?

1. ....

2. ....

3. ....

4. ....

5. ....

A gentle warning about getting addicted to workshops and brain candy: you already know so much more than the average person. Your listening skills and natural intelligence are what makes you a powerful Health Counselor, not how many books you've read or degrees you have. Further your education for fun and for your own interest, not because you think you don't know enough.

NEED MOTIVATION?

If you lack motivation, look inside and be honest with yourself about what you are experiencing. Why have you not been prioritizing health counseling? Only you know the answer to that question. If you aren't sure, journal about what you are going through and get feedback from your mentor, buddy and other support people.

In our experience, lack of motivation is often caused by fear of success or failure. Deep down you want to be a Health Counselor, but you lack confidence for one reason or another. You probably have thought patterns from a long time ago that still go on in your head and say that you aren't good enough or smart enough to do what your heart desires.

A helpful analogy here is the Hudson River. Everyone thinks it flows one way, downstream into the ocean. But the river is very deep and influenced by tides. Although it's hard to tell on the surface, the river's flow actually changes direction several times a day, sending water back upstream. This is similar to what happens inside of you when you say you want something, but underneath it all you are too afraid. Powerful feelings can pull you in the opposite direction from where you really want to go. Take a moment to think about any fears you have around being a Health Counselor. Know that it is totally normal to have these fears.

COMMON FEARS STUDENTS FACE

- I'm not healthy enough, so who am I to be telling other people what to eat and how to exercise?
- If I actually succeed at this, then I'll have to be perfect all the time.
- If I work for myself, I'll always be thinking about work.
- If I make money, I'll have to support everyone else in my family.
- If I outgrow my old lifestyle, I'll lose all my friends.
- It's not safe to depend on myself for a paycheck. I could go broke.
- If I do what I want instead of what my parents want, they won't love me anymore.
- What if my clients don't get well? They might blame me and be angry.
- If I own a business, I will lose free time and flexibility.
- I'm not smart enough to make good decisions, so my business could fail.
- If I spend all day listening to people talk about their problems, I'll feel depressed.
- If I get up in front of people and talk about nutrition, people will laugh at me.
- If I'm always helping other people, no one will help me.
- If I change careers, I will lose credibility with my business associates.
- If I do what I want to do, everyone will think I'm selfish.

Make a list of potential reasons why you might not want to be a Health Counselor.

1. ....

2. ....

3. ....

4. ....

5. ....

6. ....

7. ....

8. ....

9. ....

10. ....

Notes:

It is worthwhile to spend some time acknowledging your fears. See if you can decipher where these fears originated. Remember that the past is over and anything is possible in the present. Use your counselor, a journal and the support at the school to work through your fear, procrastination and self-doubt.

On occasion, people simply are not motivated to be Health Counselors because it is not their calling in life. They may come to the school and start out as Health Counselors, but end up deciding that becoming a full-time mom is where their true happiness lies, or that their lifelong dream is to move to another country. Whatever your dreams are, we want them to come true. Know that even if you don't have clients in a six-month program, you will always be a source of inspiration and health to those who know you.

CAREER FUTURE-BUILDING

What would you like to accomplish in your career by the end of the week?

....

....

....

....

What would you like to accomplish in your career by the end of the month?

....

....

....

....

Notes:

What would you like to accomplish in your career by the end of the year?

....

....

....

....

....

....

What would you like to accomplish in your career in 2 years?

....

....

....

....

....

....

What would you like to accomplish in your career in 5 years?

....

....

....

....

....

....

What would you like to accomplish in your career in 10 years?

....

....

....

....

....

....

What would you like to accomplish in your career in 20 years?

....

....

....

....

....

....

Beyond:

....

....

....

....

....

....

The principal motivating factors in life are goals. If you do not have them, you won't know what you are working toward. Regardless of where your passions lie—either in health counseling or another career—setting goals for your future provides motivation. Then you must do the work to turn these dreams into your reality.

CREATE YOUR FUTURE

There is a direct correlation between your thoughts and the future you create for yourself. The more confidently you move forward with your business, the more victory will come to you.

Whatever your goals are, act as if you have already accomplished them. Carry yourself as if you have the number of clients you want. Talk to potential clients as if you know they are going to sign up for your program and that it is going to be one of the best things that ever happened to them.

Every time you catch yourself thinking that this might not work out, change your thought to something more positive. When an opportunity to expand your business comes your way, jump on it! Don't let potential clients, referral partners or leads get by you. Trust your instincts when it comes to people. And when your gut tells you that there is an opportunity coming your way, take it and then give gratitude. Gratitude is a way of thanking the universe and inviting more opportunities.

Notes:

List three things you feel confident and positive about right now.

1. ....

2. ....

3. ....

REFLECTING ON YOUR ACCOMPLISHMENTS

Building your health counseling business is a journey, not a destination. It is not a problem that has to be solved, but rather a process through which you will learn what being successful means and looks like to you. If you can develop the habit of recognizing your accomplishments along this journey, you will have the added bonus of experiencing joy. When you stop to recognize how well you are doing, you put focus on your own prosperity and invite in even more. One way to appreciate your progress is to take an inventory before bed each night, and appreciate everything you did well that day. Another way is to post your to-do list or Big Rocks somewhere in your office, and when you have accomplished something, check it off the list. By doing this you will see exactly how much you have done. Consistently remind yourself that you are an amazing person, and you are doing the best that you can.

FOCUS ON OPPORTUNITIES NOT OBSTACLES

Successful people focus on opportunities, not obstacles. They see potential growth, not potential loss. It comes down to the age-old question, "Is the glass half empty or half full?" We're not talking about positive thinking here; we're talking about your habitual perspective on the world.

You don't want to make choices out of fear, to constantly be scanning for what could go wrong in any situation. Successful people expect to succeed. Try to be optimistic. Act upon the mindset, "It will work because I'll make it work." Have confidence in both your abilities and creativity, and believe that, should things get messy, you can find another way to succeed.

If you want to experience success, focus on the opportunities in everything. If you focus on opportunities, they will come to you. If you focus on obstacles, they will be all around you. Your field of focus determines what you find in life.

Try this as your motto: action beats inaction. Successful people get started. They trust that once they get in the game, they can make intelligent decisions in the present moment, make corrections and adjust their skills along the way.

Adapted from *Secrets of the Millionaire Mind: Mastering the Inner Game of Wealth* by T. Harv Eker, Harper Business, $19.95.

What are you most proud of regarding your health counseling business?

....

....

....

....

....

....

What has been your greatest accomplishment in the past six months?

....

....

....

....

....

....

What obstacles have you overcome to be where you are today?

....

....

....

....

....

....

What concrete benefits have you brought to your clients, friends, family and to yourself as a result of committing to health counseling?

....

....

....

....

Notes:

Notes:

List 10 things you love about yourself.

1. ....

2. ....

3. ....

4. ....

5. ....

6. ....

7. ....

8. ....

9. ....

10. ....

GRADUATE PROFILE

LISA GRAHAM
New York, NY
lgrahamlin@yahoo.com
2004 Graduate

looking to eat healthier, lose weight and use nutrition to prevent disease. I am always thinking of new ideas and ways to network. I am affiliated with a spa and work there one evening a week as a Health Counselor. I also recently incorporated image consulting into my practice.

I have a college degree in fashion, and it is one of my passions. Everyone has an individual personal style and I love helping people find what it is. I give them tools to work with their body type and portray an image that is in line with their goals. It is a natural extension of health counseling, and it blends into my business beautifully.

> "Anything is possible if you put your mind to it and take consistent action."

Getting clear around money and my worth as a Health Counselor was a crucial part of my process. Originally, I charged $100 per month and I steadily increased my price to $300 per month. I am confident about my program and feel comfortable charging this rate. My guidance and support are worth it. It feels good to do what I love and get paid well for it.

It is really beneficial to deal with money at the first session and get payment for the entire program up front, whether in one lump sum or post-dated checks. It gets too confusing and inconvenient if I don't take care of it at the beginning. If I'm going to work with someone, I need them to be 100 percent committed. Paying up front keeps my clients focused and dedicated to the program.

I love health counseling because I can support people and see their lives change for the better. Minor changes make huge differences, and giving a little knowledge goes a long way. I continue to learn and improve myself as I teach my clients to learn and improve themselves. Anything is possible if you put your mind to it and take consistent action.

G rowing up, I was involved with exercise and sports, but I never paid attention to what I was eating. When I was diagnosed with optic neuritis, which is associated with multiple sclerosis, I realized that my poor eating habits were affecting my health. I was eager to learn as much nutrition information as possible, so when I came across the Integrative Nutrition catalog, it sounded perfect for me.

At the school, I became clear about my passions and where I wanted to go with my career. I know what it's like to be scared about my health and to feel there is nowhere to turn when doctors are not helpful. As a Health Counselor, I support people in the process of exploring alternative routes, listening to their body's signals, and using food to restore their health and vitality.

I work full-time as an executive assistant in a real estate development company and run my health counseling business part-time during evenings and weekends. My clients are primarily busy professionals who are

We can achieve what we can conceive and believe.

—*Mark Twain*

CHAPTER 10:

ACHIEVING AND SUSTAINING
A FULFILLING CAREER

As you near the end of the PTP, you are probably making some decisions about where to take your health counseling practice. Will this be a part-time adventure, to make supplemental income on top of your current career? Will you use health counseling only with your family and community without earning money from it? Or will you make health counseling your full-time job that provides income and fulfillment for years to come? This chapter has helpful information no matter where you are with health counseling, but it focuses on how to develop the skills you need to be a long-term, full-time Health Counselor.

BUSINESS OWNER MENTALITY

It is a high priority for us to have our alumni experience tremendous success with health counseling long after graduation. After all, the way we are going to change the healthcare system in America is by having our graduates work with as many people as possible.

If you enjoy helping clients and can see yourself doing this work full-time, you will eventually have to shift from having a private practice, with one to 15 clients at a time, to being a business owner. People with a private practice focus on the few clients they have, do marketing and networking to maintain a number of clients they enjoy and invest minimally in business growth.

By becoming a business owner, you are saying to yourself and the world, "This is what I want to do with my life." You make health counseling your career and commit to doing this work for an extended period of time. You work to grow, enhance and stabilize your business over the long term.

One way to measure if you are ready to become a full-time Health Counselor is to look at your finances. Have you been able to easily pay your bills over the past six

Notes:

months with the money you've made from health counseling? If so, you are definitely ready to move forward, knowing it's only going to get better from here. If you haven't been able to pay your bills easily, it's probably best to focus on getting more clients before jumping into heavy-duty business building. Be sure to make a budget and financial projection plan, and assess when the right time for you to be full-time is. You can use the business revenue plan in Chapter 7 to guide you.

Taking on the mentality of a business owner can actually decrease stress. This may seem counterintuitive, but think about it. Everyone knows all businesses take a few years to build. You can approach your business slowly and methodically. The ebbs and flows of your business growth should be expected. Every corporation and business expert knows that you can't implement all your ideas for change at once. They strategize the best moves to make, measure the success of those moves and then decide the next move.

Approach your health counseling business in the same way. Once you decide to pursue this work full-time, pick one area you want to focus on. Stay on top of this point of focus. For example, you may want to increase your visibility, so you book workshops and put more effort into your PR. Do this for a month or two and measure your results. Is your phone ringing more often? Do you have more health histories this month? What worked and what didn't work? Once you evaluate this strategy, decide your next move. Always keep in mind that your business is a constant work in progress and you don't have to do it all at once.

RAISING YOUR RATES

Graduation is a perfect time to raise your rates. You can raise them by a little or a lot, depending on your comfort level and what you are already charging.

Remember when you were little and learning to ride a bike? First you rode with training wheels and eventually your mom or dad took the wheels off. When you rode without them for the first time you probably realized that you could have taken them off much sooner. Your body already knew how to balance perfectly on the bike. It was your mind that needed longer to develop confidence. Raising your rates is like taking off your training wheels. It's like saying to yourself and the world, "I can do it!"

It's time to take the training wheels off your business. Your program is priceless and has been from the first time you sat down with a client. But you needed time to develop confidence. Now you are ready to openly own your value and charge what you are worth.

In our experience $195 to $250 per month is a good amount to charge as a newly graduated Health Counselor. Maybe you are comfortable with charging more or less than that. Wherever you are is okay, but be careful not to undersell yourself. Many students and graduates have shared that when they charged $150 per month it was harder to get clients than when they increased their rates to $250. This is because $250 per month is a better indicator of the true value of the program. When people hear that it costs that much, they understand that it must really be valuable.

KEYS FOR ACHIEVEMENT

- Focus on your goals. Use the time management tools to ensure that you are using your time to work towards your top priorities.

- Evaluate how you are doing. Be honest with yourself. Are you working too hard or not hard enough? Have you accomplished enough this week, and are you able to take a day off without guilt? Constantly measure your level of effort and compare it to your results. This will help you refine your tactics and make smarter decisions.

- Complete your Big Rocks, and include scheduling workshops, networking events and marketing steps each week. If you complete everything on your Big Rocks, you will see results.

- Set up reward systems for yourself to stay motivated. Try not to have these involve food. Maybe you get a massage with every new client you sign, or if you reach your target for new clients at the end of the month, you buy yourself a new outfit. Remind yourself why you are doing this work, and set future goals to keep you working.

- Have someone else in your life who will hold you accountable for completing certain tasks and for keeping you on track to finish your future goals. They could be your buddy, your counselor or your board of directors.

- Get a different point of view on your progress or challenges. Just hearing your problem restated by another person can give you insight that might help you find a solution. When you are feeling low, it's also great to have someone as your personal cheerleader.

- No matter where you are in your business development, having a mentor and a support team is essential to your success. You may use friends, spouses or family members for this purpose, but if you are determined to do this work full-time, having a business coach is extremely beneficial. There are many experienced graduates available to help you navigate through your journey. Our graduate directory, newsletter and Case Histories book are great resources for finding successful graduates.

- A lot of opportunities will come your way as a Health Counselor. It is important to stay focused on what you want to achieve, and prioritize the things that will help you reach your goals more quickly. A rule of thumb employed by many successful graduates is to prioritize the things that bring in clients.

- Whenever things get stressful or dull, remember that you are the boss, and you can reinvent yourself and your business, so add fun activities to your routine. Take a class on something you always wanted to learn. Try a new food or recipe and then share it with your clients. This work never has to be monotonous. And, at the end of each day, appreciate yourself for your efforts and for doing your best.

Adapted from *Get Clients Now!: A 28-Day Marketing Program for Professionals, Consultants and Coaches* by CJ Hayden, $13.57.

Notes:

What do you charge for your program now?...

What services do your clients get for that cost?

....

....

....

....

....

....

List results your clients have received from working with you so far. List benefits your friends and family get simply by having your presence in their lives. What would you pay a professional for these benefits and results?

....

....

....

....

....

....

....

List everything that has gone into making you the invaluable counselor you are today. Include natural talents, unique skills, career experience, travel, personal growth and development, books you have read, workshops attended, formal education and anything else in your life. How much would you pay a professional with this level of experience to be your support person?

....

....

....

....

....

....

If you asked your biggest fan how much you should charge for your program, what would they say?

....

....

....

....

....

What will be the new cost of your program when you graduate?

....

....

....

....

....

SETTING FINANCIAL GOALS

As a business owner, you no longer have a boss setting your salary. You get to decide how much money you want or need to make, and then make it happen. Your financial plan helps you determine how many clients you need to see at a given time, which helps you organize your marketing plan. Financial planning can be fun and empowering as you learn to take charge of your money in a new way.

List your monthly personal expenses:

Rent/mortgage: $ ....

Food: $ ....

Clothing: $ ....

Entertainment: $ ....

Health insurance: $ ....

Self-care: $ ....

Other household expenses: $ ....

$ ....

$ ....

Notes:

$ ....

$ ....

$ ....

$ ....

List your monthly business expenses:

Phones: $ ....

Internet: $ ....

Office supplies: $ ....

Client giveaways: $ ....

Cooking class materials: $ ....

Other event expenses: $ ....

Taxes: $ ....

Other: $ ....

$ ....

$ ....

$ ....

$ ....

$ ....

$ ....

How much would you like to save or invest per month? $ ....

Add up all these expenses. This is how much you want to make per month: $ ....

Multiply by 12. This is your desired yearly income: $ ....

How much will come from your health counseling business? $ ....

How much will come from other ventures? $ ....

How many clients will you need? ....

1. List the amount that will come from counseling each month: $ ....

2. List your monthly program fee: $ ....

3. Divide line 1 by line 2: ....

This is the number of clients you need to see each month in order to reach your desired income.

For example, if you want to make $6,500 from health counseling this month, and you charge $295 per month, you will need to see 22 clients this month to make the income you desire. Revisit your marketing strategy to see how it can help you to meet your goal in an efficient, effective way.

HEALTH INSURANCE

As a self-employed person, you will have to purchase health insurance yourself if you need it. Most health insurance options for small businesses and sole proprietors are expensive, but as today's workforce becomes more mobile and flexible, new options are being created all the time. Plans often vary by state, so research options in your area and keep an eye out for any new plans that might offer you a better deal.

INDIVIDUAL PLANS WITH MAJOR INSURERS

You don't need to be employed by a big company to be covered by popular providers like Blue Cross Blue Shield, HIP, Aetna and others. You can buy an individual plan directly from the providers. HMO options are usually the most affordable, ranging from about $300 to $500 a month. In general, the higher your deductible, the lower your monthly premium and vice-versa. Visit each company website to get specific prices for plans.

PLANS FOR FREELANCERS AND SOLE PROPRIETORS

Because many self-employed people cannot afford to buy their insurance from the big companies, cities or professional groups sometimes pool their resources to offer basic plans at more affordable rates. For example, in the New York City area you can purchase insurance through Healthy New York (healthyny.com), and outside of New York City, you can find plans through Working Today's Freelancers Union (workingtoday.org). Monthly premiums for an individual run between $200 and $300, but you can also buy coverage for family members.

COVERAGE THROUGH ANOTHER EMPLOYER

If you have a spouse or close relative with a good insurance plan at their job, you can be covered on their plan. This could cost the same or more as paying for your own basic insurance, but you might get more benefits or more flexible options. Also, if you are health counseling part-time and working somewhere else part-time, your employer may be able to cover your health insurance needs.

HIRING HELP

To run a thriving business, you are going to need support. Help can come from your family, friends and support team. It should also come from paid professionals. It is worth it to invest in yourself so that you can have a great life and get your agenda accomplished. Your paid employees and support people are there to help you do just that.

HIRING AN ASSISTANT

If you have a solid practice and are consistently making $75 to $100 per hour, you can hire an assistant. This person will take care of basic tasks, like typing and filing, for $12 to $15 per hour, leaving you much more time to market your business and sign clients. Most likely you will not need your assistant to work full-time. You can set up hours that work best for you. They could come in one full day each week or for a few hours each day. Delegate those tasks that take time away from signing clients and ones that you don't need to do in person. Depending on your needs, your assistant could organize your papers, order supplies, book appointments, buy your groceries or research new places for you to give workshops.

HIRING ADDITIONAL HEALTH COUNSELORS

Signing up too many clients is a good problem to have. If you want to keep a high number of clients in your business, but you can't handle seeing all of them, hire another Health Counselor.

Here's how this can work. Do health histories and close deals with clients, letting them know that you will assign them to a counselor in your business that best suits their needs. Then pay another counselor to work with some clients. Negotiate an agreement with your counselor about how much they will be paid. Will you pay them hourly or give them a percentage of the fee? This is completely up to you.

If and when you hire other counselors, you may want to incorporate education into their benefits. You can take them to time management or personal growth and development conferences to help them improve their counseling and business skills. You can also provide self-care benefits like organic meals in the office, weekly yoga classes or monthly massages. Having other counselors in your business can be very rewarding. Your team can have lunch together, discuss client health concerns, share laughs and disappointments and generally support one another.

HIRING OTHER PROFESSIONALS

What are other areas of your life where you could save time, money and energy by paying someone to help you? For example, is it worth it to spend five hours cleaning your home this week? Or could you use that time to sign more clients and pay someone $100 to clean your house? Is it worth it to spend extra time commuting across town for your yoga class? Or could you hire a yoga instructor to come right to your door?

Professionals you could hire include:

- Accountant
- Bookkeeper
- Business coach
- Cook
- Cleaning person
- Massage therapist
- Private yoga instructor
- Writer or writing coach

If you are a new business owner, you might feel uncomfortable being "the boss" and paying others to do what you ask. Actually this is a great way to practice knowing your own worth and being "on top of the food chain." Recognize that you are up to something exciting that others will want to be a part of. Many people would love to work for a passionate, committed business owner who runs their practice with love and integrity and who is making the world a better place. Over time you will figure out a management style that works best for you. Build your confidence by leading your team and noticing that other people are happy to support you.

GIVING BACK

Chances are your life is pretty good. You may only see what is not working for you. In reality, many people in the world are hungry, sick, poor and live without a home or a family. When you realize how others are living and compare it to how you are living, you'll see that most people in the world would love to have your life.

We encourage you to find ways to give freely to those who have less than you. In your local community there may be senior citizens, children, people with illnesses or underprivileged families who would benefit greatly from your services and cannot afford them. Sharing your expertise with those less fortunate can be hugely rewarding for you, and they will benefit from access to priceless information they would not have if not for your services.

Ways you can give back:

- Work with a school to offer an inexpensive group program to teens.
- Donate free sessions, cooking classes or workshops to a benefit auction.
- Organize a group of volunteers to cook a healthy meal for a soup kitchen.
- Work with a YMCA or community center to offer a group program for free or at reduced rates.

Notes:

- Ask your local church, school or retirement home if they would like you to give a free talk about wellness.
- You can also give to community organizations that are working on important health issues.
- Grassroots organizations are often volunteer-run and under-funded. They could benefit greatly from your time, expertise or financial donation.

Movements you can support:

- Advocating for clean air and water.
- Protecting the quality of organic foods.
- Raising public awareness about the dangers of sugar and junk foods.
- Fighting the influence of the food industry on the government and media.

SCHOOL FOOD

One area that many of our graduates are involved with is school food. Today people are more aware than ever that sugar, junk and low-quality foods are hurting our children. Parents and community groups are starting to press for more nutritious foods in schools so that our children can be healthy and have a great future.

In spring 2006 the government ruled that sugary soft drinks could no longer be sold in elementary and middle schools. By summer 2006 all schools nationwide had to have wellness policies. These steps are a great start, but there is a lot more to do. Schools and parent groups need active support to learn what foods are healthy for their children and how to get those foods into school cafeterias.

EXPAND YOUR HEALTH COUNSELING CAREER

- Run retreats.
- Write a book.
- Get a radio show.
- Get a cooking show.
- Own a wellness center.
- Create your own magazine.
- Work in a hospital or doctor's office.
- Be a corporate wellness consultant.
- Be a school food expert or activist.
- Get a column in a newspaper or magazine.

How to help the schools:

- Offer free wellness workshops directly to kids.
- Drop by your local school at lunchtime and see what the kids are being fed.
- Ask the head of the PTA what is already being done to improve school food.
- Offer free wellness workshops to PTA members, school administrators or concerned parents.
- Find out what your state and local government says about school food and organize a letter-writing campaign.

Resources for supporting the healthy school food movement:

- www.ecoliteracy.org/programs/index.html
- www.healthyschoollunches.org (for New York State)
- www.angrymoms.org (by Integrative Nutrition graduates)

Giving generously to people and organizations that need support can be an important part of fulfilling your vision. The more you understand that the universe supports you to achieve your dreams and to always have enough, the easier it is to share your time, energy and expertise with others.

MACRO-VISION

In Chapter 1 we talked about your vision for your practice. Please revisit this vision. It's helpful to break this down into a macro-vision and a micro-vision. A macro-vision is similar to a mission statement. It is the ultimate goal of your business and maybe even your life. Your macro-vision drives all the choices you make. It answers the questions of why you were born and what impact you want to have on the world. Your macro-vision is bigger than you are.

Here's an example: The macro-vision for Integrative Nutrition is to transform the healthcare system in America and throughout the world to make the world a happier, healthier place. Take a moment now to write out the macro-vision of your business.

Use the vision exercise from Chapter 1 and the mission statement exercise from Chapter 4 to help you.

....

....

....

....

....

Notes:

Now refine your macro-vision. See if you can express it in just two or three sentences.

....

....

....

....

....

....

MICRO-VISION

Your micro-vision is what you will focus on in the coming months to make your macro-vision a reality. It answers the question of what you are going to do today to support your macro-vision. For example, if your macro-vision is to improve the quality of life for children in your community, your micro-vision may be to get involved in local schools and create a plan to upgrade school lunches.

As a Health Counselor, many projects and opportunities will come your way. Your micro-vision helps you make day-to-day choices about what to get involved in. Gauge each opportunity that comes your way and only take on projects that are a match for you. Know that it is okay to turn down opportunities if they are not in alignment with your vision. In some cases you may be offered projects that are in line with your macro-vision but not your current micro-vision. It is okay to postpone those projects until a later date.

Your macro-vision will stay more or less constant throughout your life and practice. Your micro-vision will shift every few months as you complete projects, expand your horizons and discover new ways to meet your goals. Revisit your micro-vision often to make sure it is still relevant and helping you to fulfill your overall vision.

Write down your micro-vision for your business in the next six months.

....

....

....

....

....

....

LIFELONG LEARNING

Notes:

One of the most effective ways to build and maintain your business is to stay connected to the Integrative Nutrition community. You will have access to educational tools and programs designed especially for graduates, including alumni OEFs, Local Study Chapters, the alumni newsletter and teleclasses.

The best way to stay connected to the school is the Immersion Program, which is our second-year program. This program offers unparalleled training and support as part of an elite group of students, who take their life and business to the next level. We are excited to offer this opportunity to any students who qualify. As an Immersionist, you will: deepen your counseling skills and client expertise, develop your confidence and self-esteem, get advanced support in building your business, experience amazing personal growth, develop lifelong friendships with other like-minded people and create a life you love, with purpose and clarity. Most graduates participate right after their PTP year to maintain their momentum. You will receive information in class and by email to learn how to apply to the program.

Integrative Nutrition is a community of people working together to affect great change in the world. We strongly recommend you surround yourself with other graduates. Your Health Counselor friends are invaluable. They will be able to listen to you and offer you the business and personal advice that only other Health Counselors can give. Please stay connected to the people and resources you need to continue to learn and grow.

WE APPRECIATE YOU

We know that you had to overcome a lot to make it to Integrative Nutrition. For many of you it has meant reprioritizing your life, traveling long distances or letting go of personal fears and limitations. We truly appreciate you for dedicating yourself to making this world a happier, healthier place to live. Thank you for all the hard work you put into being a student. Thank you for being a part of our community. We are proud to have you as a graduate of our school and hope you will stay connected and continue to work with us to make our vision a reality. We wish you a happy, healthy future, filled with great success.

GRADUATE PROFILE

ROBIN PEGLOW
Denver, CO
robin@signsoflifehealth.com
2000 Graduate

I used to be a staff recruiter for a summer camp in upstate New York. I wasn't making the kind of impact I wanted to in the world; I knew I wanted to live a bigger life. When I first heard about Integrative Nutrition, I wasn't sure if I wanted to go, but the more I thought about it, the more I realized that health counseling was the perfect career for me.

My year at Integrative Nutrition was the best year of my life. It was great to be part of a community that was really up to something. The school taught me to honor myself, dream big and choose my own life. It had been my dream to live in Colorado, and after graduation I made it happen.

My health counseling practice focuses on supporting women to discover their "soul food," that which nourishes inspiration, intuition and rebalances the feminine within strength. Most of my clients are women who are generally happy in their lives, yet have a subtle sense that there is something more, a deeper experience available to them that they're not sure how to find. They're often motivated career women and moms who've hit a sticky spot of "Now what?"

My program is a formula for helping these women access their wisdom and intuition, so they can begin living the kind of life they desire—one that will make them truly happy. I have created a series of classes called "Access Your Power Within™" that support women in aligning with their goals, values, intuitions and inspirations. In just over three years I have led 70 women through this program, and it's great to see the difference it has made in their lives. Based on this work, I wrote, and now sell *Power On Purpose: A Daily Guide to Living in Your Power,* a self-care guide and companion book.

> "Learn to let go of your fear and be graceful in the face of uncertainty."

I used to call myself the best kept secret in Denver, but that's no longer true. I knew only two people when I arrived here, and I built my business from scratch. Since then, I've been interviewed for the TV news and published in several magazines, reaching well over 30,000 subscribers. My network of supporters and referral partners has grown substantially. And now I'm positioning myself to support even more people by running retreats and expanding my publications.

One of the challenges of building a practice is that we often don't know exactly how it's going to be or what to expect. Learn to let go of your fear and be graceful in the face of uncertainty. Be willing to let things evolve. We often want it to happen right now, but many lessons must come slowly. It takes time to lay the foundation.

I do this work because it energizes me, and because I love supporting people to get inspired. I am fostering relationships in my workshops and creating a more conscious community in Denver. My business is going incredibly well and totally expresses who I am. I'm so grateful, and I can't imagine doing anything else.

INDEX